W9-AQX-252

These tanks are filled with octopi.
Which octopus does not appear in both tanks?
Circle it.

Deduction

These scenes are filled with butterflies.
Which butterfly appears in both scenes?
Circle it.

Deduction

Write the names of the toys on the left.
Write the names of the animals on the right.

cat ball cow top dog doll

Toys

Animals

_____   _____

_____   _____

_____   _____

Deduction/Categorizing

Look at the word list.
Circle the words in the puzzle.

saw bee pie jet car bed

U K B N M B S D Y
T S A W F E K H P
Q M F D X D J G M
Y F Z O F W B H J
K L V Q Z L E W P
F P I E W G E F B
X K W B F Q U J N
J W C A R W T E S
A U Y W M K L T O

Look at the word list.
Circle the words in the puzzle.

cat dog pig fox bug cow

A P U C D X K L A
W C A T K Y T F G
K H D Z G Z V O L
F D B D S T V X V
K J X O W C O W R
B M N G Z X C K J
C Y G X N P I G W
K W S D W P U Q L
G B U G F S V F R

Word Search

Compare Pictures A and B.
Find and circle 9 things that are different in Picture B.
Color the pictures.

Picture A

Picture B

Compare Pictures A and B.
Find and circle 9 things that are different in Picture B.
Color the pictures.

Picture A

Picture B

Comparing and Contrasting

Compare Pictures A and B.
Find and circle 9 things that are different in Picture B.
Color the pictures.

Picture A

Picture B

Comparing and Contrasting

Compare Pictures A and B.
Find and circle 9 things that are different in Picture B.

Picture A

Picture B

Comparing and Contrasting

Compare Pictures A and B.
Find and circle 9 things that are different in Picture B.

Comparing and Contrasting

ICE CREAM PARLOR

Compare Pictures A and B.
Find and circle 9 things that are different in Picture B.

Picture A

Picture B

Comparing and Contrasting

Compare Pictures A and B.
Find and circle 9 things that are different in Picture B.

Picture A

Picture B

14

Compare Pictures A and B.
Find and circle 9 things that are different in Picture B.

Comparing and Contrasting

Susan has lost her cat.
Find the cat that matches the one in her picture.
Circle it.

Comparing and Contrasting

POND PALS

There are many frogs at the pond.
There are two frogs that are the same. Circle them.

Comparing and Contrasting

BUSY B WORDS

Look at the word list.
Circle the words in the puzzle.

bird boat ball bus bed bee book

```
N B L B X K Y D S
K I F G B O A T H
P R Z L X N W K B
G D R B D B V H A
P V M U K E Q N L
Z W Q S F E O W L
Y R B Z G K T X R
P M D S B O O K B
B E D X Q L W B Z
```

18

DIVINE D WORDS

Look at the word list.
Circle the words in the puzzle.

Tongue Twister
Dancing dolls delight!

dog dad drum duck doll dish day

Q	W	R	T	U	P	B	F	D
O	D	B	M	L	J	D	M	O
W	O	X	D	P	W	D	J	L
R	G	Q	A	B	S	R	Z	L
P	T	W	Y	S	H	U	K	P
M	D	U	C	K	X	M	X	J
G	Q	W	M	N	F	R	P	K
S	Y	G	D	J	D	A	D	B
B	D	I	S	H	H	K	C	F

Word Search

Write the first letter of each picture's name.
Read the animal's name.
Write the number in the box next to the correct animal.

1. _____ _____ _____ _____

2. _____ _____ _____ _____ _____

3. _____ _____ _____ _____ _____ _____

PERFECT PETS

Write the first letter of each picture's name.
Read the animal's name.
Write the number in the box next to the correct animal.

1. _____ _____ _____

2. _____ _____ _____

3. _____ _____ _____ _____

4. _____ _____ _____ _____

Initial Consonants

HEAVENLY H WORDS

Look at the word list.
Circle the words in the puzzle.

Tongue Twister
Happy hippos hug!

hat horn ham hook house heart hen

Word Search   ©School Zone Publishing Company

PLEASANT P WORDS

Look at the word list.
Circle the words in the puzzle.

pig puppy pear pizza penny pie pen

W P I E Q P O L P
C Q S N O I M V U
S P I G H Z L T P
Z B Q M D Z Y W P
E J C X Z A N V Y
P Z W K R T Q K H
E R G H P E N C M
A T W N C Y S R T
R W P E N N Y F X

23

Write the **short a** words for the pictures.

Short a sound: **apple**

fan bat pan hat

1.

2.

_____

_____

3.

4.

_____

_____

5. Add **ad** to make **short a** words.

h _____ m _____ s _____

6. Add **an** to make **short a** words.

m _____ r _____ c _____

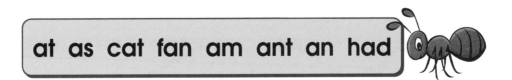

at as cat fan am ant an had

1. Write the **short a** words that have two letters.

_____ _____ _____ _____

2. Write the **short a** words that have three letters.

_____ _____ _____ _____

Spell **short a** words by adding the **short a** endings.

3. **at**	4. **am**	5. **an**	6. **ad**
b ___ ___	h ___ ___	r ___ ___	b ___ ___
h ___ ___	j ___ ___	m ___ ___	d ___ ___
m ___ ___	s ___ ___	p ___ ___	h ___ ___
p ___ ___	r ___ ___	f ___ ___	m ___ ___

Words with Short a

Color the **short e** words blue.

Short e sound: **nest**

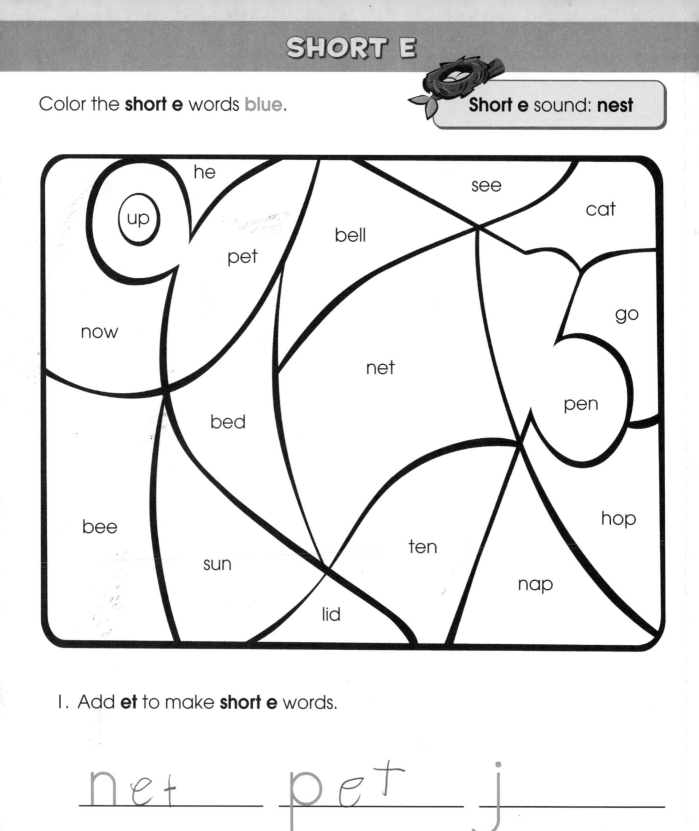

he

see

cat

up

bell

pet

go

now

net

pen

bed

bee

hop

ten

sun

nap

lid

1. Add **et** to make **short e** words.

net   pet   j

2. Add **en** to make **short e** words.

he   m   t

Words with Short e

©School Zone Publishing Company

Write the **short e** answers to the riddles.

ten bell red sled nest bed

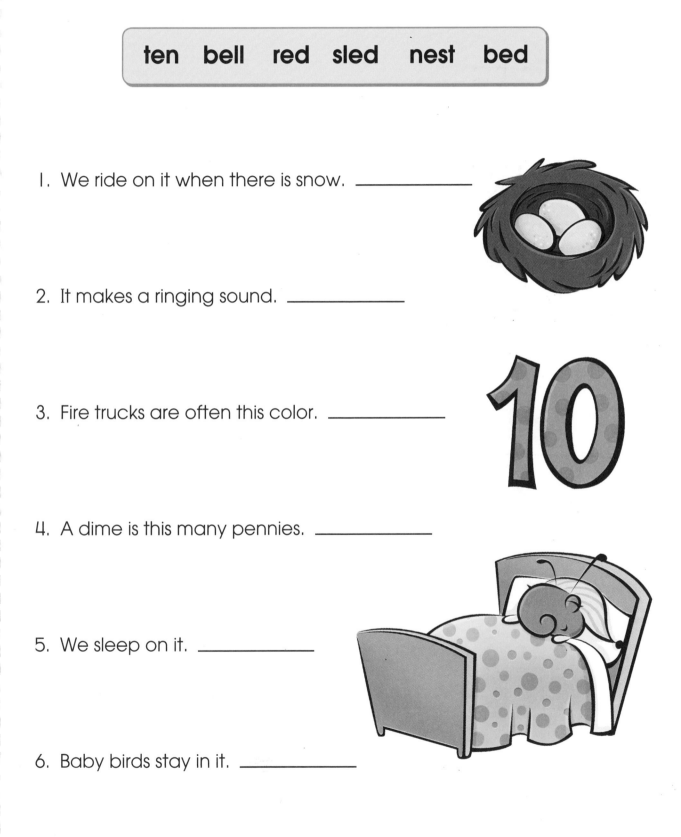

1. We ride on it when there is snow. _____

2. It makes a ringing sound. _____

3. Fire trucks are often this color. _____

4. A dime is this many pennies. _____

5. We sleep on it. _____

6. Baby birds stay in it. _____

Words with Short e

Write the **short i** words for the pictures.
Hint: They're opposites of "out" and "hers".

Short i sound: **igloo**

| big dig in pig wig his |

1.

out

_____

2.

hers

_____

3. Write the **short i** words that end with **ig**.

_____   _____

_____   _____

Words with Short i

Write **i** in the blanks to make **short i** words and to finish the silly sentences. Read the sentences to a friend.

1. I h___d the l___d, I d___d.

2. I w___ll f___ll the h___ll with flowers.

3. The b___g p___g ate a f___g.

4. I w___sh the f___sh were still in the d___sh.

Add the missing letters to make the **short i** words from the sentences above.

5. ___**id**	6. ___**ill**	7. ___**ig**	8. ___**ish**
___**id**	___**ill**	___**ig**	___**ish**
___**id**	___**ill**	___**ig**	___**ish**

Words with Short i

Write the **short o** words for the pictures.

Short o sound: **octopus**

| hot doll not fox tot box |

1.

2.

_____   _____

3. Write the **short o** words that end with **t**.

_____   _____   _____

4. Write the **short o** word that rhymes with **fox**.

_____

Write the **short o** words to answer the riddles.

rock box sock dock lock clock

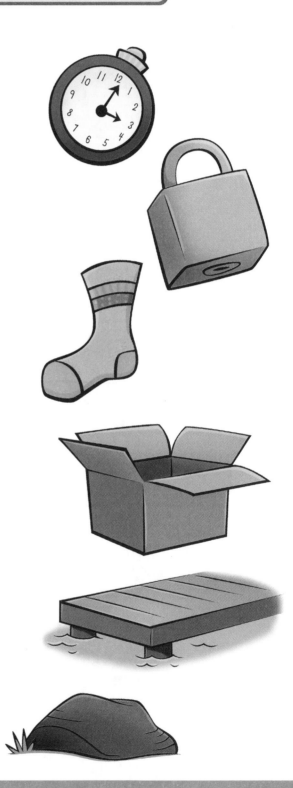

1. It tells you the time.

   _____

2. A key opens it.

   _____

3. You wear it on your foot.

   _____

4. You put things in it.

   _____

5. A boat can be here.

   _____

6. It is hard.

   _____

Words with Short o

Write the **short u** words for the pictures.

Short u sound: **umbrella**

bus cup bug sun run duck

1.

2.

_____

3.

_____

4.

5.

_____

6.

_____

Write the first letter of each picture's name to spell **short u** words.

bug gum hug cup fun mud sun pup

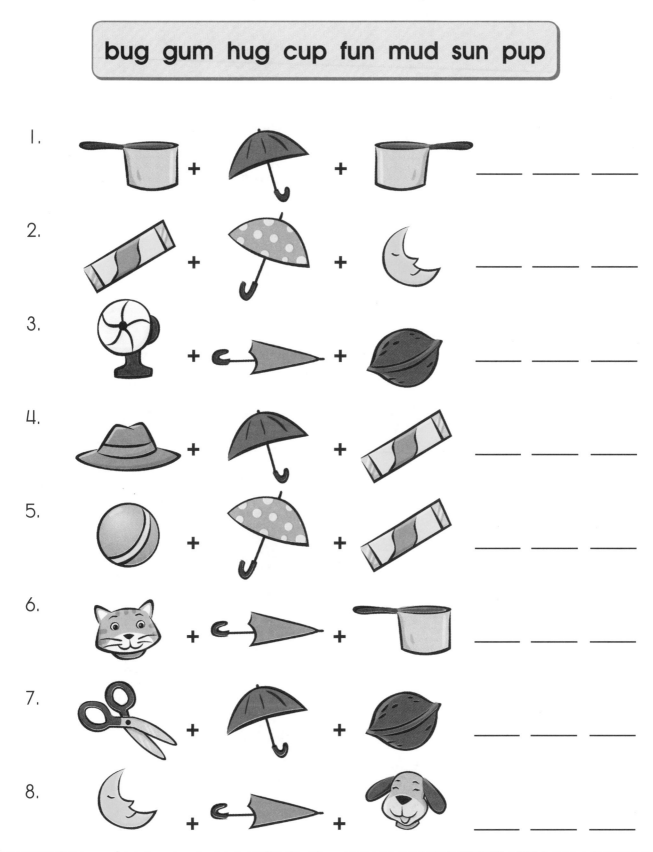

1. ___ ___ ___

2. ___ ___ ___

3. ___ ___ ___

4. ___ ___ ___

5. ___ ___ ___

6. ___ ___ ___

7. ___ ___ ___

8. ___ ___ ___

Words with Short u

Say the names of the pictures.
Circle the pictures whose names have the short vowel sounds.

1. **short a**

2. **short e**

3. **short i**

4. **short o**

5. **short u**

Short Vowel Review   ©School Zone Publishing Company

Finish the words by filling in the missing short vowels.
Each word has the same short vowel sound as the picture.
Write the words under the correct vowels on the word list.

1. s__n
b__s

2. c__t
m__n

3. h__n
r__d

4. t__p
h__p

5. p__g
b__g

Short a
_____
_____

Short e
_____
_____

Short i
_____
_____

Short o
_____
_____

Short u
_____
_____

Short Vowel Review

Write the short vowel words for the pictures.

gum bed pin top bug cat

1.

2.

3.

4.

5.

6.

Short Vowel Review

©School Zone Publishing Company

Use the clues to solve the puzzle.

sun egg pig sock ten hat

Across

2. Which word has the same vowel sound as "dock"?
3. Which word rhymes with "men"?
5. Which word has the same vowel sound as "dig"?

Down

1. Which word has the same vowel sound as "sat"?
2. Which word has the same vowel sound as "fun"?
4. Which word has the same vowel sound as "leg"?

Short Vowel Review

Write the **long a** words to answer the riddles.

Long **a** sound: **rain**

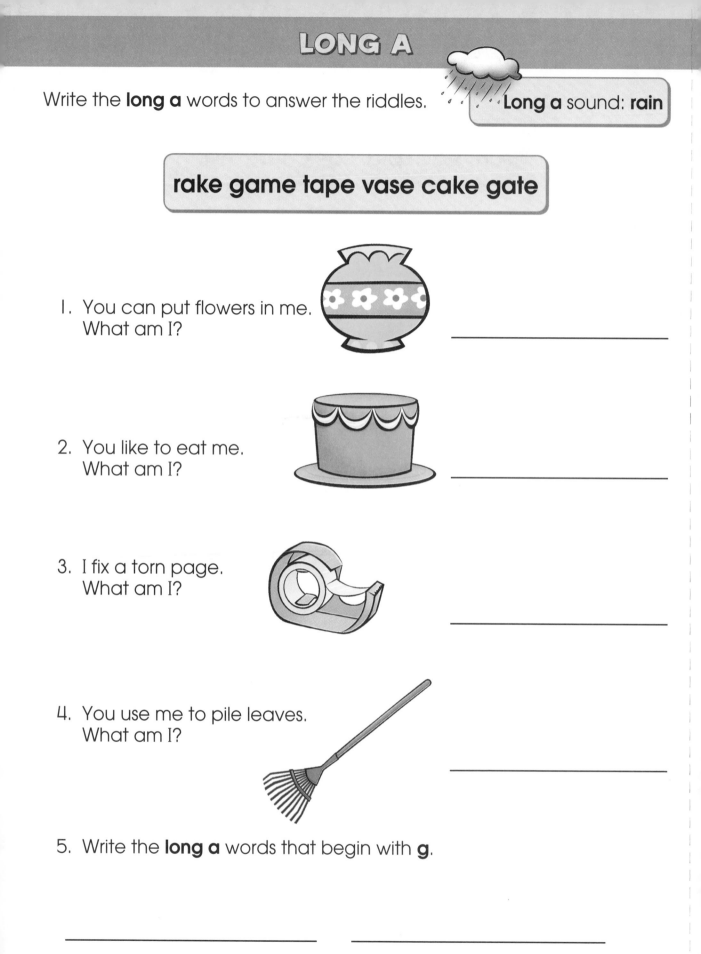

rake game tape vase cake gate

1. You can put flowers in me.
   What am I? _____

2. You like to eat me.
   What am I? _____

3. I fix a torn page.
   What am I? _____

4. You use me to pile leaves.
   What am I? _____

5. Write the **long a** words that begin with **g**.

_____   _____

Draw a line through the long a words in each puzzle.

1

so	bow	cake
hat	cab	rake
look	hook	tape

2

are	toy	pan
play	day	say
cub	tie	an

3

hid	way	cap
mad	vase	hop
new	race	pet

4

pay	cup	ham
goat	may	cow
bat	cold	hay

39

Words with Long a

Use the clues to solve the puzzle.

Long e sound: **bee**

dream clean money bean leave tree key seed see

Across

2. Produces a plant
5. Go away
7. Used to buy things
8. A kind of vegetable

Down

1. A large plant
2. Look at
3. Happens when asleep
4. Opposite of dirty
6. Opens a lock

Write the **long e** words to answer the riddles.

| bee seal me tree he leaf |

1. I can swim.
   What am I?   _____

2. I am a large plant.
   What am I?   _____

3. I grow on a tree.
   What am I?   _____

4. I get food from flowers.
   What am I?   _____

5. Write the two-letter **long e** words.

_____

_____

Words with Long e

LONG I

Write the **long i** words to answer the riddles.

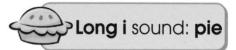 **Long i** sound: **pie**

kite tie fine bike like ride

1. You can fly me.
   What am I?

   _____

2. You can ride me.
   What am I?

   _____

3. I am something to wear.
   What am I?

   _____

Write the **long i** words that fit these shapes.

4.

5.

6.

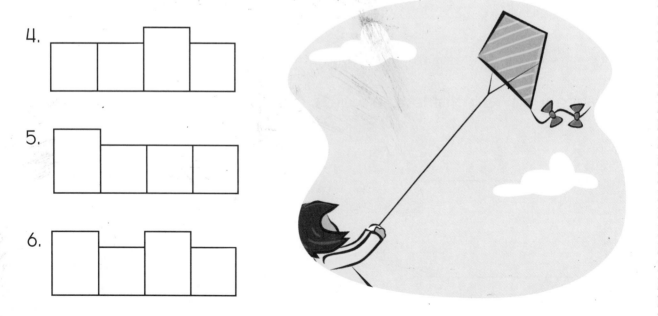

42

Words with Long i

©School Zone Publishing Company

kind find try night cry right

1. Write the **long i** words that end with **d**.

_____   _____

2. Write the **long i** words that rhyme with **kite**.

_____   _____

3. Write the **long i** words that end with **y**.

_____   _____

4. Underline the **long i** words in the story.

My friend and I took a hike up a hill.
We flew our kites high in the sky.
My friend and I had a fun time.

Words with Long i

Write the **long o** words to finish the sentences. **Long o** sound: **rose**

| show hold boat told grow goat note home |

1. What did the _____ say?

2. The _____ sailed across the lake.

Mom,
I went to Brenda's
to play. I will be
home at 4:30.
Love,
    Sue

3. Who _____ you the joke?

4. How high will the tree _____?

5. We saw a good _____ on TV last night.

6. The _____ has horns.

7. It is time to go _____.

8. Please _____ my hand.

Write the **long o** words for the clues.
Then read the letters in the box to answer the riddle.

own   told   slow   bow   coat   grow   goat

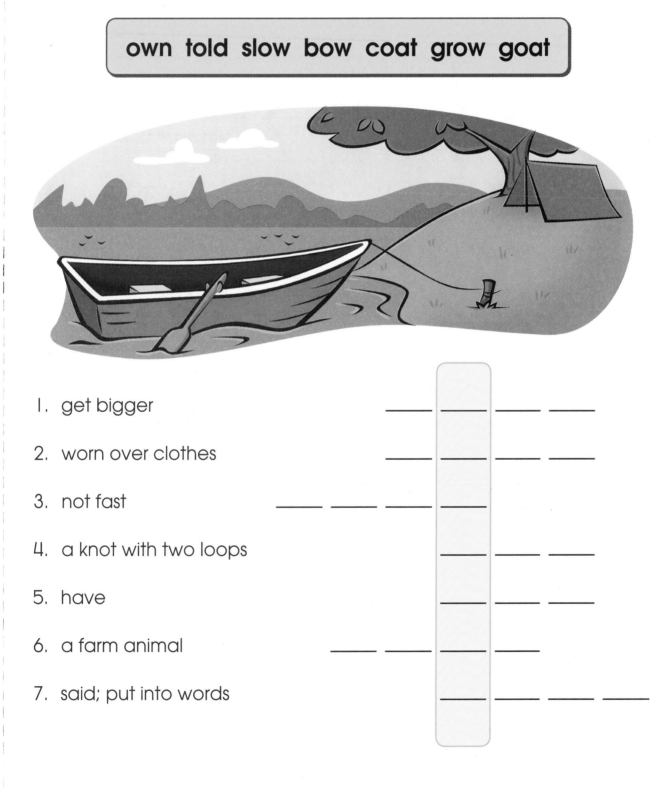

1. get bigger ___ ___ ___ ___

2. worn over clothes ___ ___ ___ ___

3. not fast ___ ___ ___ ___

4. a knot with two loops ___ ___ ___

5. have ___ ___ ___

6. a farm animal ___ ___ ___ ___

7. said; put into words ___ ___ ___ ___ ___

I float on water. What am I? __a__ _____

Words with Long o

Use the code to write the **long u** words.

Long u sound: **unicorn**

c	e	g	h	l	r	t	u	b
△	○	☆	◇	<	>	○	□	▯

cube cute huge
rule mule tube

1. △ □ ○ ○

_____

2. ○ □ ▯ ○

_____

3. ◇ □ ☆ ○

_____

4. > □ < ○

_____

Write the **long u** words for the pictures.

5. _____

6. _____

Write the **long u** words to finish the sentences.

true few cute huge view use

1. If there aren't many, there are _____.

2. If it is not false, it is _____.

3. I thought the baby was very _____.

4. An elephant is a _____ animal.

5. Standing on a mountain, you have a nice _____.

6. When you work with something, you _____ it.

Words with Long u

Color the **long a** words blue.
Color the **long e** words purple.

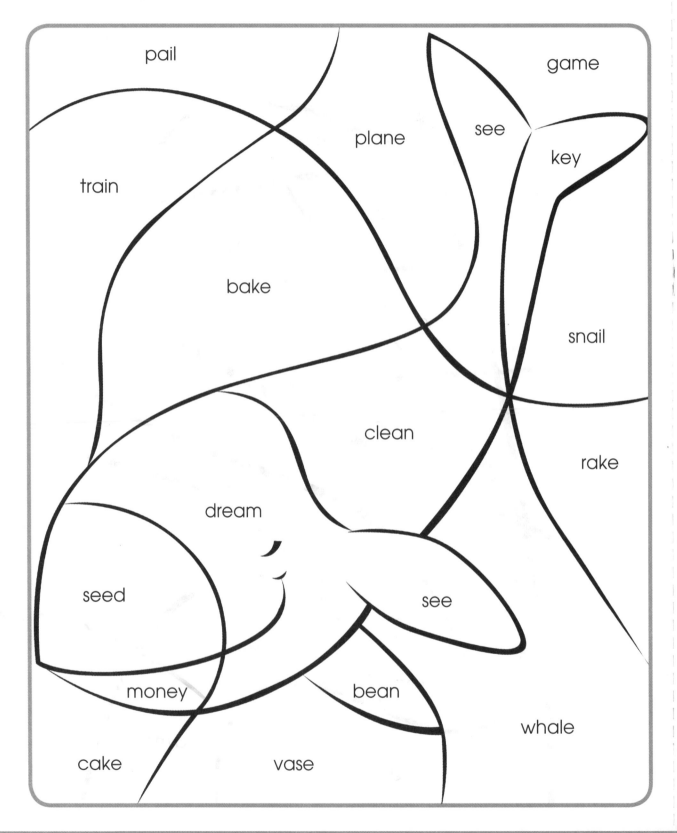

pail

game

plane

see

key

train

bake

snail

clean

rake

dream

seed

see

money

bean

whale

cake

vase

Color the **long i** words green.
Color the **long o** words blue.
Color the **long u** words orange.

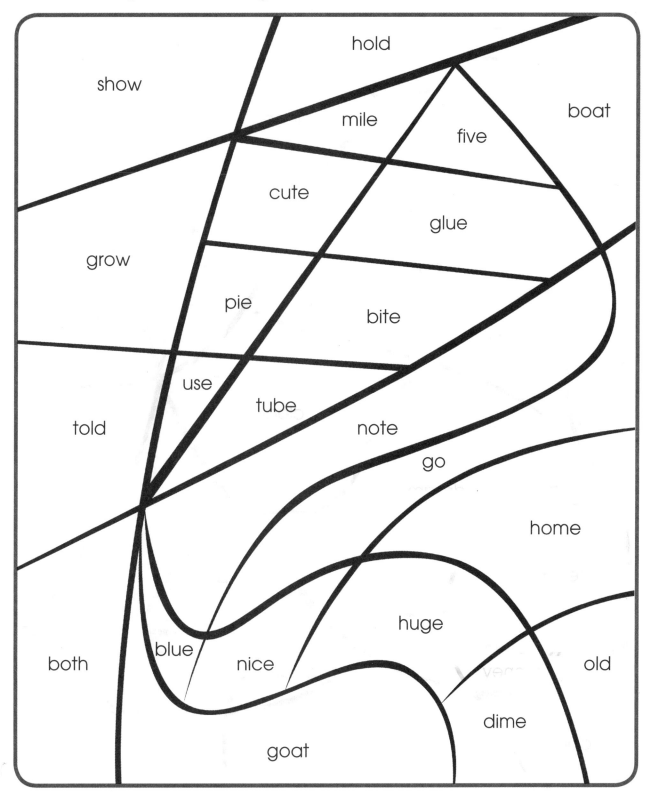

Long Vowel Review

Write the long vowel words for the pictures.

hive pie tree cake rope mule

1.

2.

3.

4.

5.

6.

Use the clues to solve the puzzle.

kite tube bee bone slide rake

 Across

1. This word has the **long a** sound.
4. This word has the **long u** sound.
6. This word has the **long i** sound and five letters.

Down

2. This word has the **long i** sound and 4 letters.
3. This word has the **long e** sound.
5. This word has the **long o** sound.

Long Vowel Review

LONG VOWEL SCENE

Color the **long a** words **blue**.
Color the **long e** words orange.
Color the **long i** words **purple**.
Color the **long o** words **brown**.
Color the **long u** words yellow.

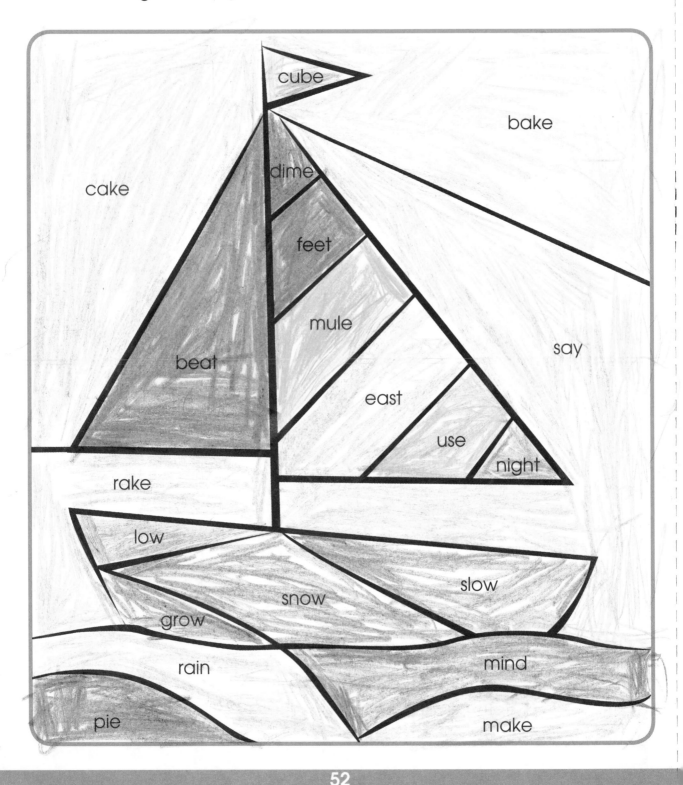

Long Vowel Review

LONG VOWEL SOUNDS

Say the words.
Circle the long vowel words.

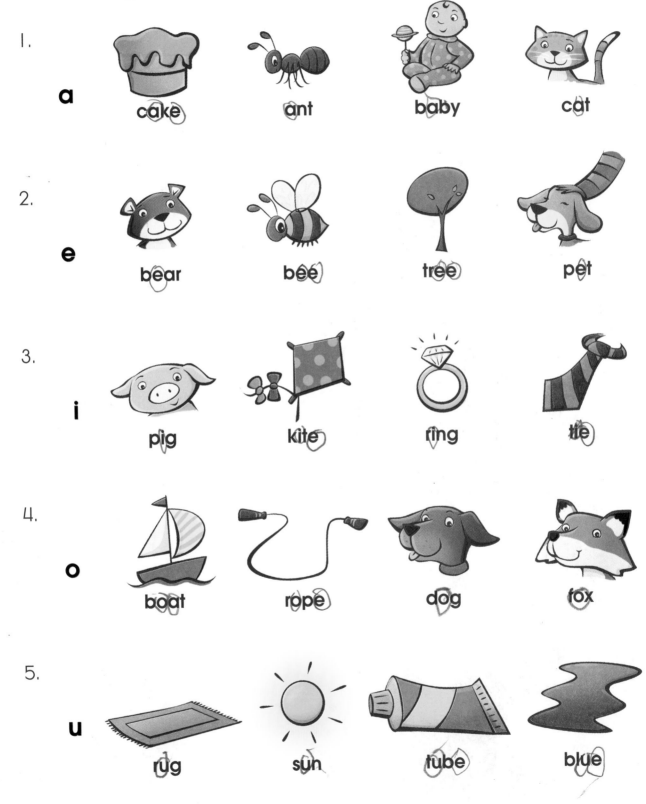

1. a

cake   ant   baby   cat

2. e

bear   bee   tree   pet

3. i

pig   kite   ring   tie

4. o

boat   rope   dog   fox

5. u

rug   sun   tube   blue

Long Vowel Rev'

COLORFUL SEA OF VOWELS

Color the long vowel fish orange.
Color the short vowel fish green.
Help the squid get to her cave.
Draw a line to connect the long vowel fish.

Short and Long Vowel Review

©School Zone Publishing Company

SHORT AND LONG VOWEL SURPRISE

Color the **short a** words blue.
Color the **short e** words red.
Color the **short i** words yellow.
Color the **Long a** words purple.
Color the **Long e** words brown.

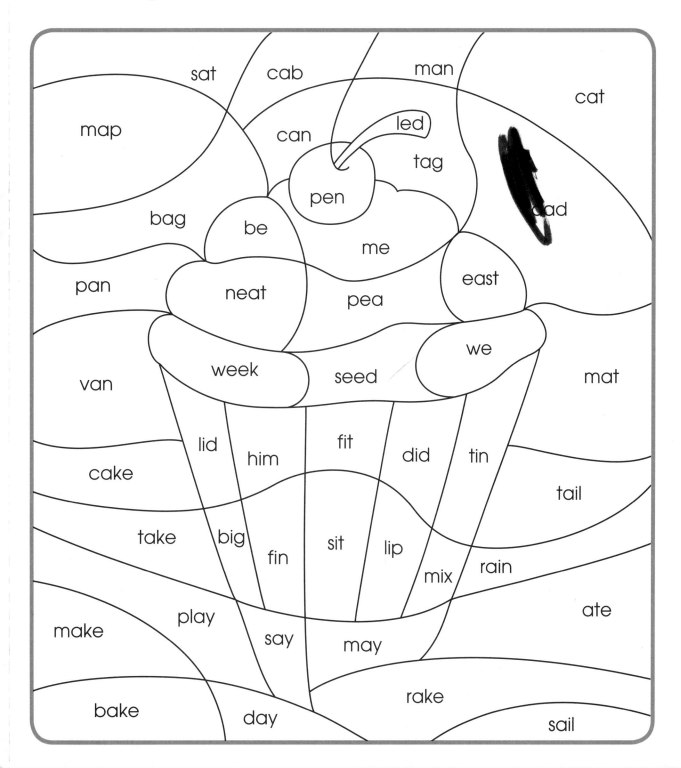

Short and Long Vowel Review

Sometimes adding an **e** to the end of a word makes a new word. The **e** on the end makes the vowel say its name.

hug → hug**e**   dim → dim**e**

Add an **e** to the end of each short vowel word to make new words with long vowel sounds. Circle the pictures of the new words.

1. **can** ___

2. **plan** ___

3. **pin** ___

4. **cap** ___

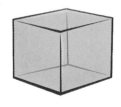

5. **cub** ___

Many words with a long vowel sound are spelled with vowel-consonant-e.

Add **e** to the words to make **long vowel** words.

1. **at** _____ 2. **kit** _____ 3. **pin** _____ 4. **hug** _____ 5. **dim** _____ 6. **mad** _____

Write the long vowel words from above to complete the sentences.

7. A whale is _____ .

8. It _____ a mess.

9. It cost a _____ .

10. How high can your _____ fly?

11. That is a _____ tree.

12. We _____ pizza for lunch.

Vowel-Consonant-e

Write the long vowel words for the clues.
Then read the letters in the box to answer the riddle.

| home dime pine those nine cute save make |

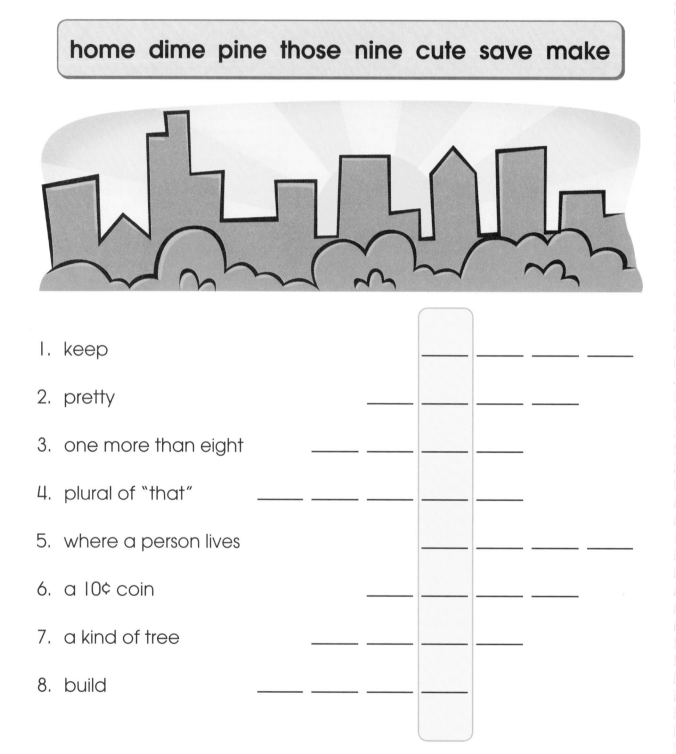

1. keep _____ _____ _____

2. pretty _____ _____ _____

3. one more than eight _____ _____ _____

4. plural of "that" _____ _____ _____ _____

5. where a person lives _____ _____ _____ _____

6. a 10¢ coin _____ _____ _____

7. a kind of tree _____ _____ _____

8. build _____ _____ _____ _____

I brighten your day. What am I? _____

IT'S RAINING R WORDS!

Look at the word list.
Circle the words in the puzzle.

Tongue Twister
Royal rhinoceroses recline!

rain ring robot rose rug red robin rope

R A I N F T Y P Q
R B S Q O W R U R
I K B J P Q O K O
N H R E D Z B R B
G K L O L J O Q I
R O S E R W T P N
V R Z Q O W Z J L
Z U I F P R H N Q
I G C Q E W F C W

59

SHINING S WORDS

Look at the word list.
Circle the words in the puzzle.

Tongue Twister
Silly snails' slime!

sock   sun   star   seal   snail   sing   soap   sit

Q D L P J S I T V
W S F M B X Y O H
Q I J K S S T A R
C N V U N W L X M
S G P M A K J B R
E Z S Q I J S U N
A Q M P L C Q P K
L S O A P I P G K
E P F T W S O C K

Write all the words that start with **sh** in the sheep pen.
Write all the words that end with **sh** in the fish pond.

push shop shoe show dish shirt shell wash wish

1. _____

2. _____

3. _____

4. _____

5. _____

6. _____

7. _____

8. _____

9. _____

Digraph: sh

CHUMMY FRIENDS

Draw lines from the words that start with **ch** to Chad.
Draw lines from the words that end with **ch** to Mitch.

fish

book

ditch

glass

cherry

man

cheese

chimney

catch

match

touch

chair

porch

watch

beach

banana

Chad

Mitch

Digraph: ch

Write the correct **th** words to finish the sentences.

> **bath   path   there   Thank   thirty   think**

1. Our dog, Rex, would not let us give him a _____ .

2. We _____ he's afraid of water.

3. Rex tried to run from us, but we followed his _____ .

4. It took us almost _____ minutes to catch him.

5. _____ goodness Mom was _____

   to help us!

Digraph: th

Write **wh** on the blanks to spell the words.

1. _____ _____ eel

2. _____ _____ y

3. _____ _____ en

4. _____ _____ eat

5. _____ _____ ale

6. _____ _____ at

7. _____ _____ istle

8. _____ _____ ite

9. _____ _____ ere

10. Circle the **wh** words in the word search.

```
W H I S T L E
H H A W H Y W
A R W H A T H
L N X I T W E
E W H T T H R
W H E E L E E
W H E A T N S
```

Digraph: wh

Write the **ch**, **wh**, **sh**, and **th** words for the clues.
Then read the letters in the box to answer the riddle.

inch branch white she whale path

1. a water animal ___ ___ ___ ___ ___

2. the color of snow ___ ___ ___ ___ ___

3. part of a ruler ___ ___ ___ ___

4. a walkway ___ ___ ___ ___

5. opposite of he ___ ___ ___

6. part of a tree ___ ___ ___ ___ ___ ___

I come after autumn. What am I? _____

Digraphs: ch, wh, sh, and th

Read the clues.
Write the combination sound answers in the puzzle.

dirty hurt hurry better bird third turtle every

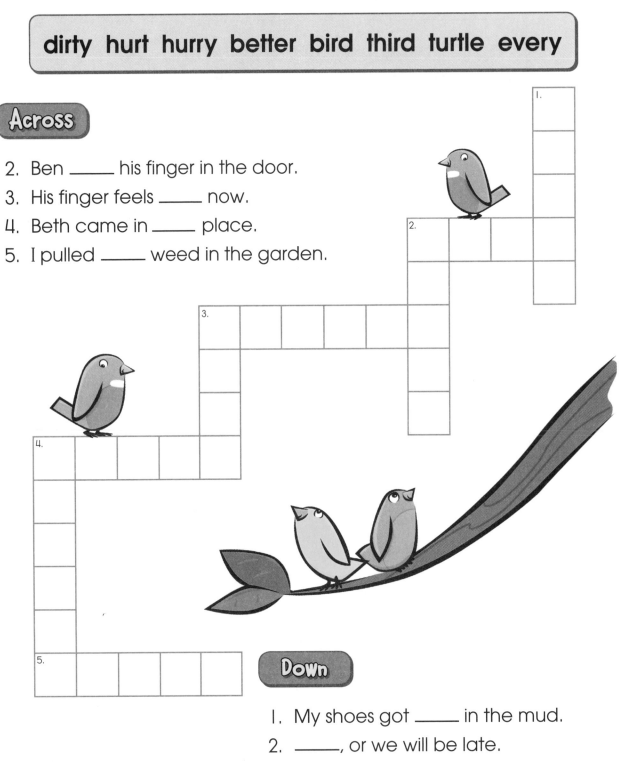

Across

2. Ben _____ his finger in the door.
3. His finger feels _____ now.
4. Beth came in _____ place.
5. I pulled _____ weed in the garden.

Down

1. My shoes got _____ in the mud.
2. _____, or we will be late.
3. If an animal has feathers, it's a _____ .
4. A _____ lives on land and in water.

Combination Sounds: er, ir, and ur

Read the story.
Underline all the **oi** and **oy** words.

Roy was in a toy store with his mother. He had saved his coins to buy a new toy. There were many kinds of toys. Some toys made too much noise. Some toys cost too much. He finally made a choice. Roy counted all his coins. He chose a toy he could enjoy with his friends.

Underline the correct answers.

1. Where was Roy?

   at home   in a toy store   at school

2. Who was with Roy?

   his mother   his sister   no one

3. Write three **oi** and three **oy** words.

   oi   **oy**

   _____   _____

   _____   _____

   _____   _____

Diphthongs: oi and oy

Read the story.
Underline all the **ou** and **ow** words.

Mom and I saw a brown mouse in our house. Our cat saw it and gave a howl. Down from his pillow, he started to run. The cat chased the mouse around the house. We opened the door to let the mouse out. It let out a squeak, and away it ran.

Underline the correct answers.

1. Which people saw the mouse?

   Mom and Dad   two friends   Mom and I

2. Which words rhyme?

   house   howl   mouse

3. Write three **ou** and three **ow** words.

   ou   **ow**

   _____   _____

   _____   _____

   _____   _____

Diphthongs: ou and ow   ©School Zone Publishing Company

Write the words for the clues.

1. You can sit on it.

_____

2. You go there to learn.

_____

3. It is the color of the sky.

_____

4. Things stick together with it.

_____

5. If there are not many, there are _____.

_____

6. It is the opposite of old.

_____

> new
> few
> stool
> glue
> blue
> school

Diphthongs: ew, oo, and ue

Write the words for the clues.

| food tool new moon zoo flew soon blue |

1. helps do work _____

2. not old _____

3. something to eat _____

4. before long _____

5. a color _____

6. seen at night _____

7. where animals are kept _____

8. rhymes with "blew" _____

Write **oo** or **ew** to make words.

9. | n | | |

10. | z | | |

11. | c | | | l |

12. | r | | | m |

13. | b | l | | |

14. | k | n | | |

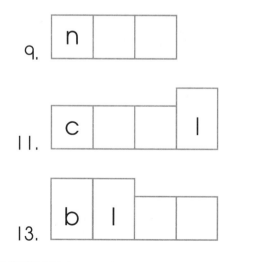
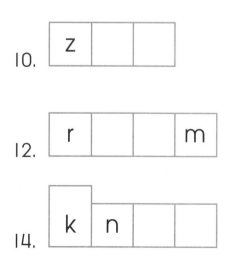

70

The letters **c** and **g** make different sounds in different words.
Copy the words. Say the words.

1. The letter **c** sounds like **k** before these vowels: **a**, **o**, and **u**.

cat _____

cow _____

cup _____

2. The letter **c** sounds like **s** before these vowels: **i** and **e**.

city _____

circus _____

cent _____

3. The letter **g** sounds like the **g** in **goat** before these vowels: **a**, **o**, and **u**.

gas _____

gum _____

good _____

4. The letter **g** usually sounds like **j** before these vowels: **i** and **e**.

general _____

gentle _____

giraffe _____

Different Sounds of c and g

Color the words that have a **c** that sounds like **k blue**.
Color the words that have a **c** that sounds like **s red**.

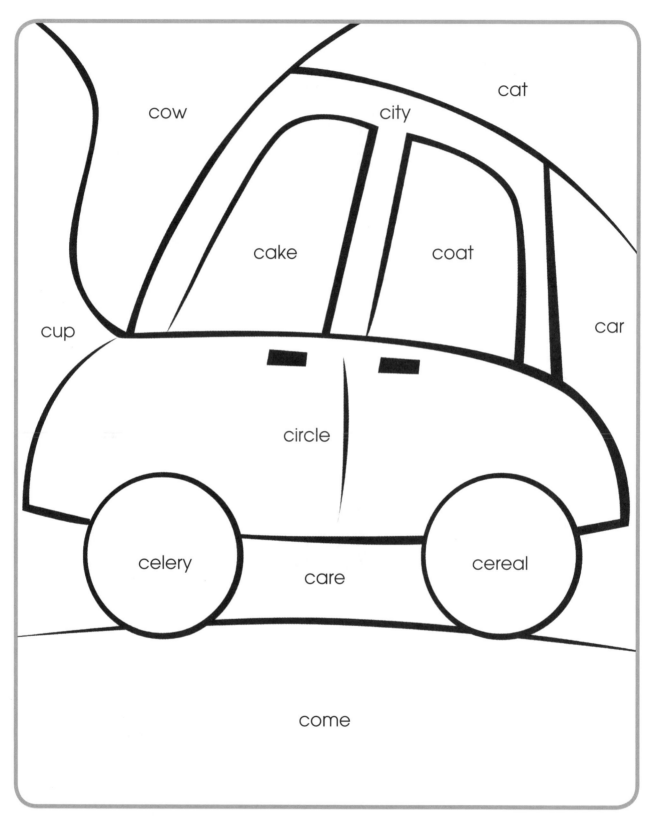

cow

city

cat

cake

coat

cup

car

circle

celery

cereal

care

come

Different Sounds of c ©School Zone Publishing Company

Color the words that have a **g** that sounds like the **g** in **goat** yellow.
Color the words that have a **g** that sounds like **g** pink.

gentle

giant

gum

good

got

giraffe

general

gas

goat

gem

Different Sounds of g

TERRIFIC T WORDS

Look at the word list.
Circle the words in the puzzle.

top   train   tent   tie   turtle   tiger   tire   toad

```
W T R A I N F L H
P K S N X Q P X T
T M T I G E R C O
E B P T M Q R T A
N J H I A R T O D
T Z Q R Z T B P I
K R G E W R Q H M
P T U R T L E J T
Z T P J N X T I E
```

74

Look at the word list.
Circle the words in the puzzle.

one two three four five six seven

Q A W G P R N T L
R O S T W O B T D
K N L N Q C N H T
T E L S I X Y R T
X C V L D R S E L
F S F O U R L E L
I R J D L K T X R
V F D S E V E N Y
E V R Y N G K B Z

75

Words that **rhyme** have the same vowel sound and ending sound.

Underline the rhyming words.

1. The king began to sing.

2. Her cat wears a hat.

3. The dog ran after the frog.

4. I wish I had a fish.

5. My coat is in the boat.

6. A vet took care of my pet.

Rhyming Words

Underline the rhyming words.

1. The pail fell in the well.

2. Look at my new book.

3. The boy had a new toy.

4. I like your new bike.

5. I was told you had a cold.

6. The pig wore a wig.

Rhyming Words

RHYMING WORD SEARCH

Look at the word list.
Circle the words in the puzzle.

hen ten bed wed van fan box fox

H	X	F	W	L	C	F	O	V
Q	H	E	N	X	Q	O	Y	A
A	D	F	Q	X	T	X	R	N
I	Z	W	J	D	W	D	T	P
P	J	E	X	F	A	N	E	K
Y	H	D	Q	T	F	S	N	T
U	T	M	K	U	D	P	N	W
Q	B	E	D	J	Z	X	T	Q
Z	S	H	K	G	X	B	O	X

RHYMING WORD SEARCH

Look at the word list.
Circle the words in the puzzle.

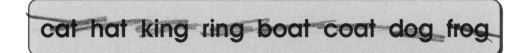

cat hat king ring boat coat dog frog

```
K C A T O H A T G
B R T X K O P T C
K K T B O A T L O
Q I N P U V K P A
Y N Z A S J S T T
O G T R I N G Q E
L N W D Z O I E D
R T F R O G K J O
C Z T D W Y S M G
```

Rhyming Words

RHYMING FUN

Change the first letter of each word to make the names of animals.
Draw lines from the names to the animals.

1. hat

   _____

2. log

   _____

3. house

   _____

4. coat

   _____

5. box

   _____

6. dish

   _____

Rhyming Words   ©School Zone Publishing Company

Write rhyming words to finish the silly sentences.
Change the first letter in the underlined words to make new words.

1. A <u>toad</u> is in the _____ _____ _____ _____ .

2. A <u>fox</u> jumped out of a _____ _____ _____ .

3. My <u>fish</u> sleeps in a _____ _____ _____ _____ .

4. The <u>bunny</u> is very _____ _____ _____ _____ _____ .

5. A <u>bug</u> gave me a _____ _____ _____ .

6. The <u>goose</u> is on the _____ _____ _____ _____ _____ .

7. The <u>king</u> lost his _____ _____ _____ _____ .

Rhyming Words

Write rhyming words to finish the silly sentences.
Change the first letter in the underlined words to make new words.

1. A <u>mouse</u> is in my ___ ___ ___ ___ ___ .

2. A <u>bug</u> <u>dug</u> into my ___ ___ ___ .

3. A <u>goat</u> is eating my ___ ___ ___ ___ .

4. A <u>hen</u> has my <u>pen</u> in the ___ ___ ___ .

5. My <u>cat</u> is in love with a ___ ___ ___ .

6. My <u>dog</u> is being a ___ ___ ___ .

7. That <u>bat</u> was in my ___ ___ ___ .

8. The <u>big</u> <u>pig</u> took my ___ ___ ___ .

Read the clues.
Write the correct rhyming words.

1. It is the opposite of cold.
   It rhymes with "not".

   _____

2. It is a pet.
   It rhymes with "jog".

   _____

3. You wear one on your foot.
   It rhymes with "rock".

   _____

4. It is a wild animal.
   It rhymes with "box".

   _____

5. It tells the time.
   It rhymes with "block".

   _____

Rhyming Words

Read the clues.
Write the correct rhyming words.

1. It is a farm animal.
   It rhymes with "dig".

   _____

2. It is the opposite of "dry".
   It rhymes with "vet".

   _____

3. It is a chicken.
   It rhymes with "pen".

   _____

4. A bird builds one.
   It rhymes with "best".

   _____

5. It is a number.
   It rhymes with "pour".

   _____

Rhyming Words   ©School Zone Publishing Company

Read the clues.
Write the correct rhyming words.

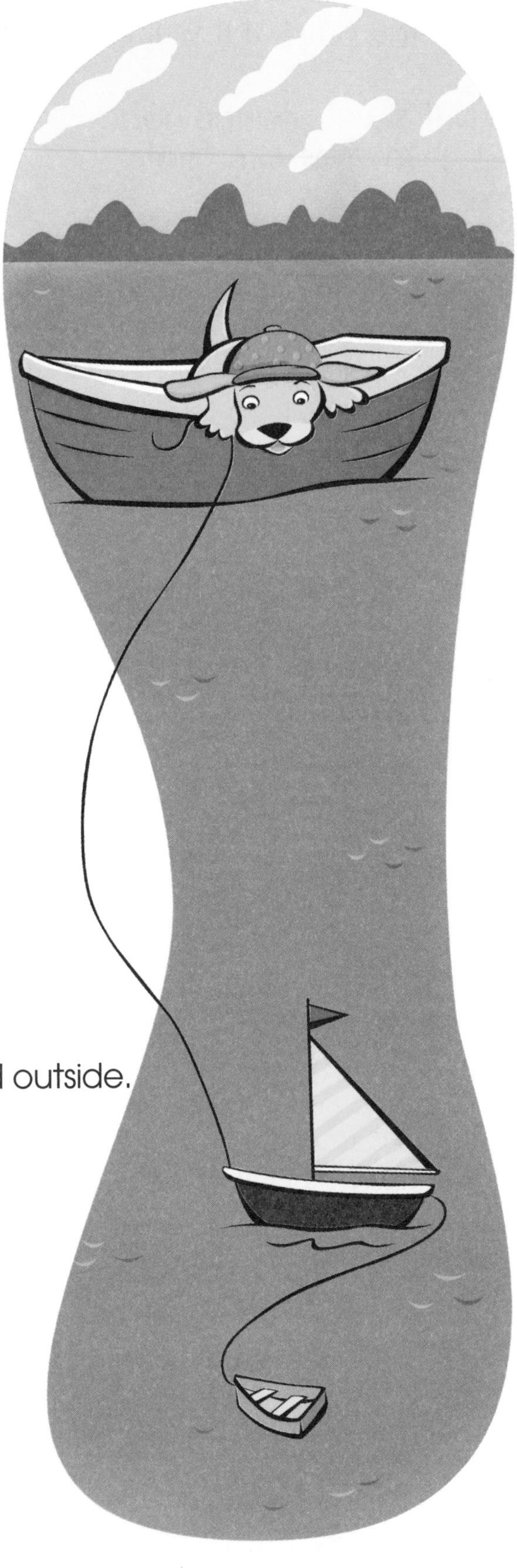

1. You sleep on it.
   It rhymes with "red".

   _____

2. It can swim.
   It rhymes with "dish".

   _____

3. You sail about on it.
   It rhymes with "take".

   _____

4. It is something to wear when it is cold outside.
   It rhymes with "boat".

   _____

5. It rings.
   It rhymes with "tell".

   _____

Rhyming Words

Read the clues.
Write the correct rhyming words.

1. It is warn on the head.
   It rhymes with "bat".

   _____

2. You play with it.
   It rhymes with "tall".

   _____

3. It is a sweet treat.
   It rhymes with "lake".

   _____

4. You ride in one.
   It rhymes with "far".

   _____

5. It is a color.
   It rhymes with "bed".

   _____

6. It is a pet.
   It rhymes with "hat".

   _____

86

Read the clues.
Write the correct rhyming words.

1. You can ride it.
   It rhymes with "like".

   _____

2. It is worth 10¢.
   It rhymes with "time".

   _____

3. It is something you fly.
   It rhymes with "sight".

   _____

4. It is the opposite of "day".
   It rhymes with "right".

   _____

5. It is a sweet desert.
   It rhymes with "tie".

   _____

6. You do it when you are sad.
   It rhymes with "dry".

   _____

Rhyming Words

RHYMING CLUES

Read the clues.
Write the correct rhyming words.

1. It is what an insect is called.
   It rhymes with "dug".

   _____

2. It is a kind of bird.
   It rhymes with "luck".

   _____

3. It takes children to school.
   It rhymes with "us".

   _____

4. It is a color.
   It rhymes with "clue".

   _____

5. It gives us heat and light.
   It rhymes with "fun".

   _____

6. It is the opposite of "old".
   It rhymes with "dew".

   _____

RHYMING CLUES

Read the clues.
Write the correct rhyming words.

1. You see this in the sky at night.
   It rhymes with "soon".

   _____

2. Bees make this in their hive.
   It rhymes with "money".

   _____

3. This animal eats cheese.
   It rhymes with "house".

   _____

4. This animal makes the milk we drink.
   It rhymes with "now".

   _____

5. This thing sails on water.
   It rhymes with "coat".

   _____

6. This is something you read.
   It rhymes with "look".

   _____

Rhyming Words

Read the poems.
Complete the poems by writing the correct rhyming words on the lines.

light   cry   me

1. Some animals hop.
    Some animals fly.
    Do some animals laugh?
    Do some animals _____?

    _____

2. I like to read books
    While I'm in bed at night.
    When I get sleepy,
    I just turn off the _____.

    _____

3. My dog runs after a squirrel
    That climbs up a tree.
    He can't reach it, so he
    Runs back to _____.

    _____

RHYMING POEMS

Read the poems.
Complete the poems by writing the correct rhyming words on the lines.

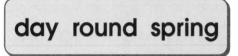

day   round   spring

1. I like the flowers growing.
   I like the birds that sing.
   I like the growing season.
   We call that season _____.

   _____

2. I like sunny days with
   Snow on the ground.
   I like the nights when
   The moon is so _____.

   _____

3. Some days are foggy.
   Some days are gray.
   I like the times when it's
   Sunny all _____.

   _____

Rhyming Words

Read the poems.
Complete the poems by writing the correct rhyming words on the lines.

white   snow   running   showers

1. Clouds fly high
   When the sun is bright.
   The very best clouds
   Are fluffy and _____.   _____

2. The hot days are best
   For swimming and sunning.
   But the cool days are better
   When I want to go _____.   _____

3. It falls from the sky
   When the cold winds blow.
   I hope it stays!
   I want to play in the _____. _____

4. April brings rain.
   May brings flowers.
   The colors in May
   Make me like April _____.   _____

Use the clues to solve the puzzle.

smile sting dress class smell drag

Across

2. I rhyme with "thing".
4. I rhyme with "mile".
5. I rhyme with "mess".

Down

1. I rhyme with "flag".
2. I rhyme with "tell".
3. I rhyme with "grass".

Rhyming Words

Use the clues to solve the puzzle.

blue orange green yellow brown red

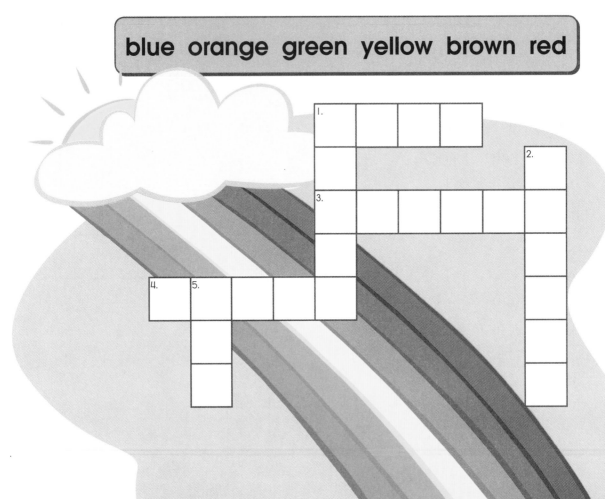

Across

1. What color rhymes with "true"?
3. What color is made with yellow and red?
4. What color rhymes with "seen"?

Down

1. What color rhymes with "clown"?
2. What color rhymes with "Jell-o"?
5. What color rhymes with "bed"?

94

Use the clues to solve the puzzle.

true trap truck tree trip trick

Across

2. What rhymes with "slip"?
3. What rhymes with "luck"?
4. What rhymes with "bee"?

Down

1. What rhymes with "clap"?
2. What rhymes with "stick"?
3. What rhymes with "blue"?

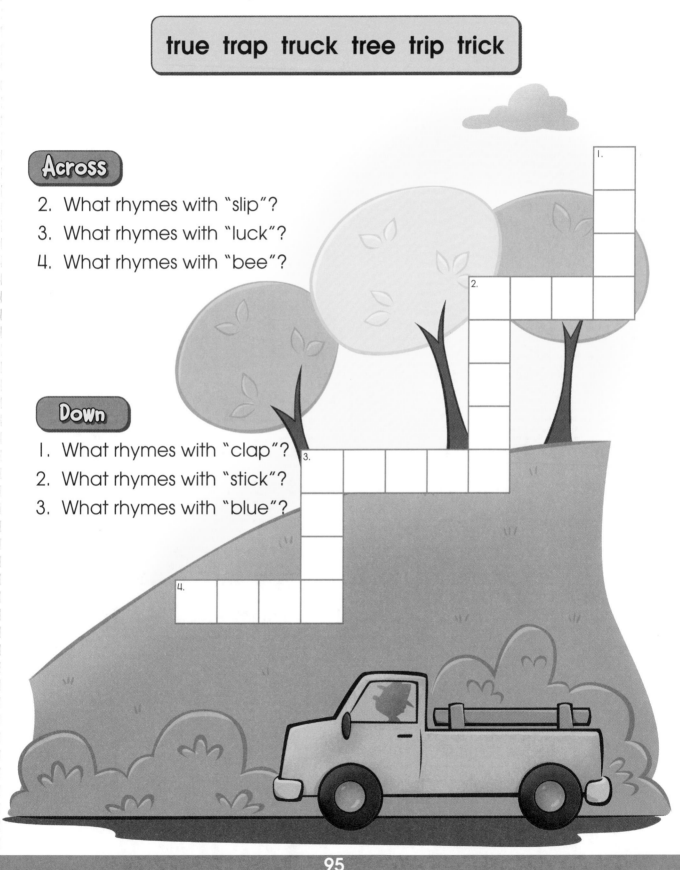

Rhyming Words

Look at the word list.
Circle the words in the puzzle.

car truck bike train bus van plane

```
P K O K M N P H X
S Q X T R A I N V
Q K H K W J C M P
T L G L C A R G L
R M G D V K B F A
U K B U S B H V N
C I S Q Z I D A E
K H Z C W K Z N H
E D Q K M E P V I
```

Look at the word list.
Circle the words in the puzzle.

carrot onion tomato corn peas celery

```
K C F C E L E R Y
B A K X Y Z P T P
W R T O N I O N R
Y R N Z U V M R O
R O M P E A S T C
V T T Q W V U Q O
O U B D J P D X R
N T O M A T O J N
S O H A Q C S B Z
```

Word Search

Happy is the **opposite** of sad.

Draw lines between the opposites.

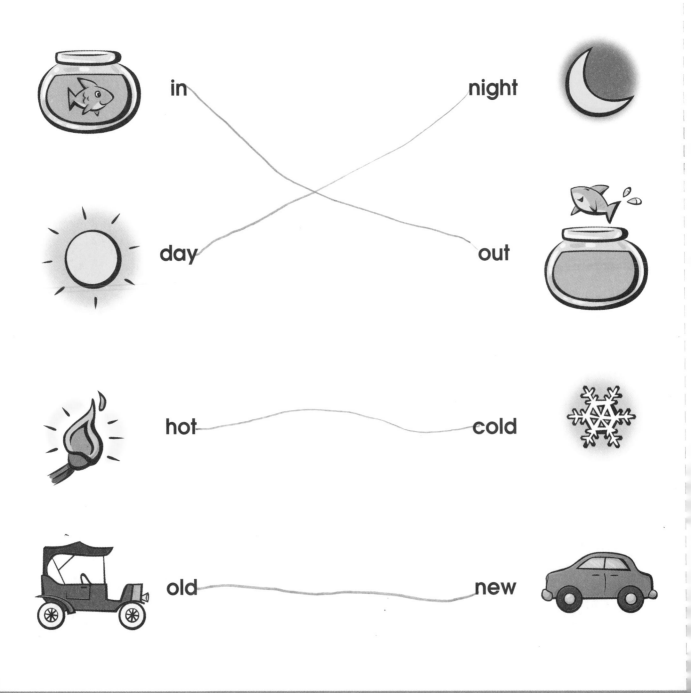

in

night

day

out

hot —————— cold

old —————— new

OPPOSITES

Draw lines between the opposites.

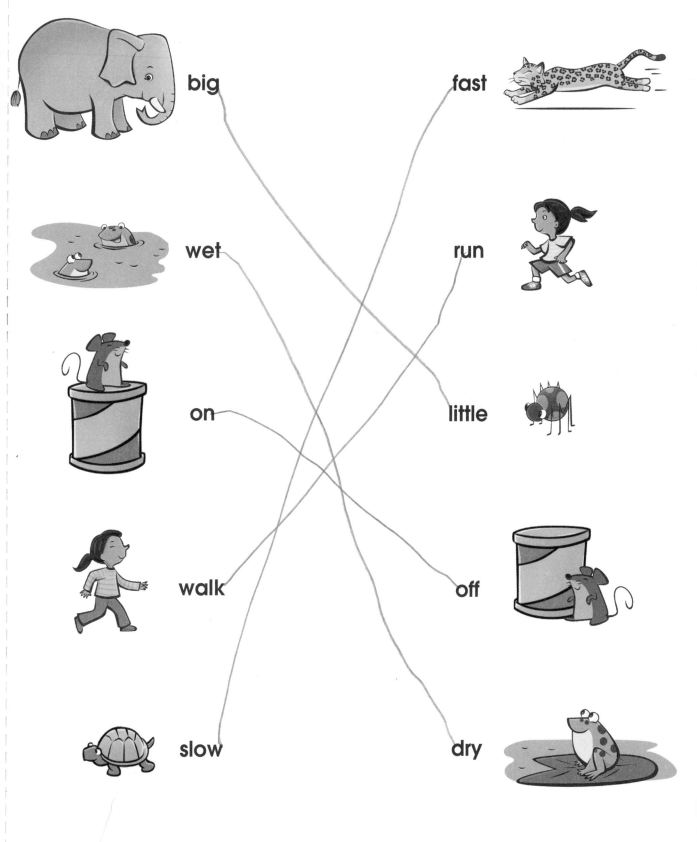

big

fast

wet

run

on

little

walk

off

slow

dry

Opposites

Draw lines between the opposites.

stop

up

short

high

over

low

tall

under

go

down

Look at the word list.
Circle the words in the puzzle.

stop go on off wet dry hot cold up down

Opposites

Look at the word list.
Circle the words in the puzzle.

big little fast slow new old in out

```
V B I G Z I N E L
O Z Q T X Q B H I
U G L N E W N P T
T U Q B N P Y O T
K X O L D R S K L
N S U Q F X L B E
A Q J D L K O X J
N F A S T Z W J Y
Z P S M N G E B Z
```

OPPOSITES WORD SEARCH

Look at the word list.
Circle the words in the puzzle.

tall short big little high low happy sad

S A D P S H O R T
K N Q V J K L Z B
H A P P Y L O W X
V N L V X C Q R T
H I G H D T A L L
N D H T F R O J M
Y R B I G K T X R
P F D Z G V N T B
X L I T T L E B Z

Opposites

FRUIT STAND

Look at the word list.
Circle the words in the puzzle.

banana cherry orange pear lemon melon apple

V T I A P P L E O
B I U Q X V B H L
A Y L E M O N N C
N U O B N W Y O H
A O P E A R I K E
N Y V P Q W K V R
A N M E L O N X R
D C V S A Z K J Y
B O R A N G E B Z

Look at the word list.
Circle the words in the puzzle.

panda seal tiger bear zebra lion elephant

```
K  P  A  N  D  A  B  C  L
S  R  T  Z  Q  O  P  T  B
T  Q  T  S  E  A  L  L  E
I  Z  B  P  U  V  M  N  A
G  B  Z  E  B  R  A  M  R
E  X  T  P  W  V  U  Q  K
R  N  B  L  I  O  N  E  H
J  T  R  D  B  W  K  J  L
M  E  L  E  P  H  A  N  T
```

Word Search

COMPOUND WORDS

Two words that are joined together to make a new word form a **compound word**.

sun + shine = sunshine

Look at the pictures.
Write the compound words on the lines.

cupcake baseball butterfly birdhouse rainbow football

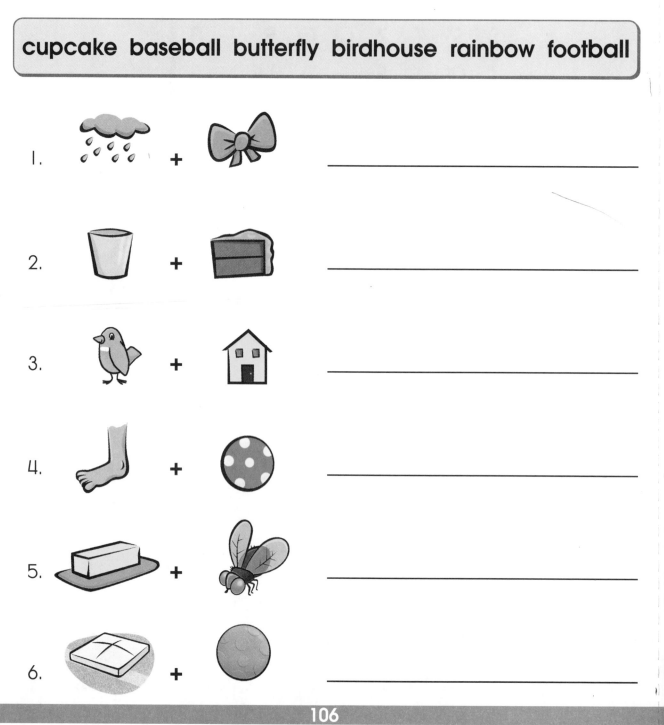

1. _____

2. _____

3. _____

4. _____

5. _____

6. _____

Look at the pictures.
Write the compound words on the lines.

sunflower starfish firefly skateboard
rattlesnake basketball doghouse

1. + _____

2. + _____

3. + _____

4. + _____

5. + _____

6. + _____

7. + _____

Compound Words

A **contraction** is two words put together.
An **apostrophe** shows where there is a missing letter or letters.

do + n**o**t = don't
we + **wi**ll = we'll

Write contractions for the underlined words.

haven't don't let's aren't won't we'll

1. Please <u>do not</u> go. _____

2. We <u>are not</u> done. _____

3. We <u>have not</u> painted it. _____

4. <u>Let us</u> paint it red. _____

5. It <u>will not</u> take long. _____

6. Then <u>we will</u> go home. _____

CONTRACTIONS

Combine the words to make contractions.

can't	it's	he'd	aren't	isn't
I'm	won't	we'll	she's	we're
don't	they're	doesn't	wouldn't	

1. does + not = _____

2. is + not = _____

3. they + are = _____

4. she + is = _____

5. can + not = _____

6. are + not = _____

7. I + am = _____

8. we + are = _____

9. do + not = _____

10. will + not = _____

11. he + would = _____

12. we + will = _____

13. would + not = _____

14. it + is = _____

Contractions

CONTRACTIONS

To undo a contraction, take out the apostrophe and add the missing letter or letters.

don't = do + n**o**t
we're = we + **are**

Add the missing letters.

1. she'll = she + w____ll

2. couldn't = could + n____t

3. don't = do + n____t

4. it's = it + ____s

5. I'm = I + ____ m

6. can't = can + ____ot

Write the words that make up the contractions.

7. doesn't = _____ + _____

8. we'll = _____ + _____

9. aren't = _____ + _____

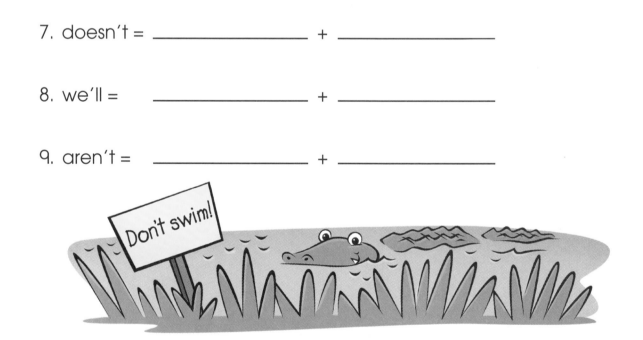

Write your own sentence using a contraction.

_____

Contractions   ©School Zone Publishing Company

IT'S COLD OUTSIDE!

Look at the word list.
Circle the words in the puzzle.

boots scarf hat coat mittens snow pants

```
W Y C S C A R F S
B Q K N D X P W N
O R H A T C V N O
O N Z T Y U O P W
T B O T X V S B P
S Q X C O A T M A
T B D P N L T J N
G K P S W Z K O T
E M I T T E N S S
```

Word Search

ORDER UP!

Look at the word list.
Circle the words in the puzzle.

hamburger hot dog pizza taco burrito fries

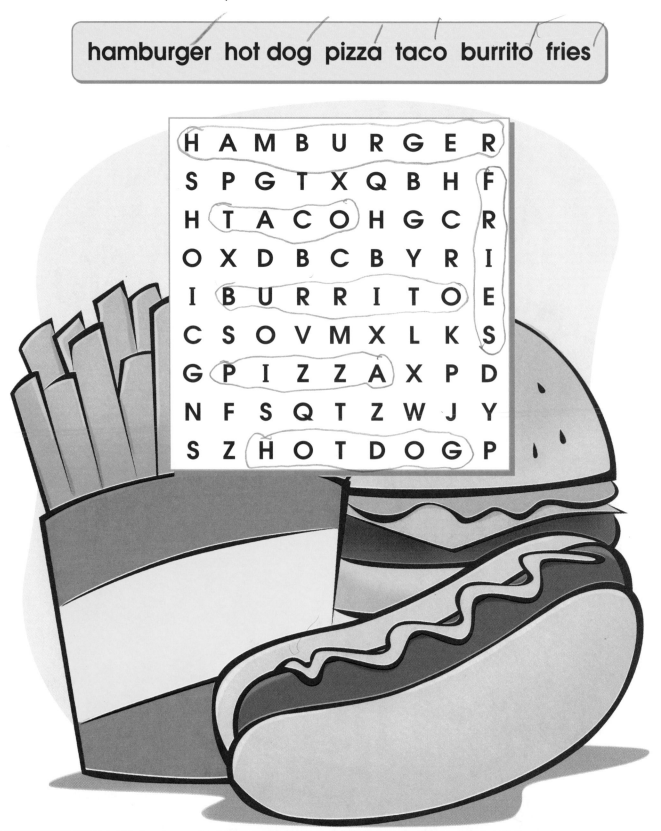

```
H A M B U R G E R
S P G T X Q B H F
H T A C O H G C R
O X D B C B Y R I
I B U R R I T O E
C S O V M X L K S
G P I Z Z A X P D
N F S Q T Z W J Y
S Z H O T D O G P
```

Synonyms are words that mean the same thing.

Happy means the same as **glad**.
Laugh means the same as **giggle**.

Draw lines to match the synonyms.

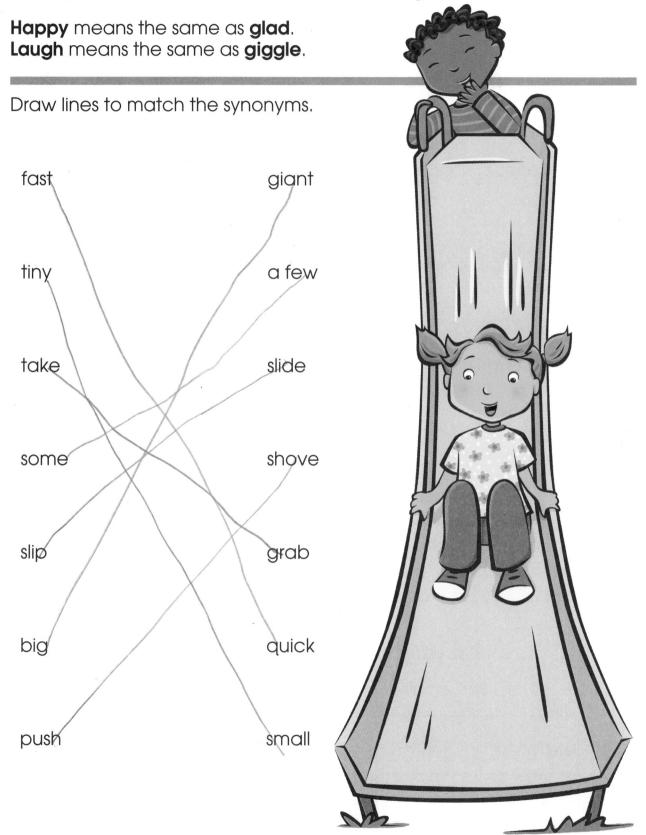

fast   giant

tiny   a few

take   slide

some   shove

slip   grab

big   quick

push   small

Synonyms

SYNONYMS

Change the underlined words to synonyms that mean the same things.

> **scared   tiny   presents   throw**

1. She opened her birthday <u>gifts</u>. _____

2. He was <u>afraid</u> of the barking dog. _____

3. The mouse was <u>little</u>. _____

4. <u>Toss</u> the ball to me. _____

Find your way through the maze by following the path of synonym for big.

start	big	funny	strong	weak	tiny	
	giant	small	massive	gigantic	grand	
	great	huge	mammoth	silly	large	
	little	happy	angry	pretty	enormous	**finish**

Synonyms   ©School Zone Publishing Company

ANTONYMS

Antonyms are words that are **opposites**.

On is the opposite of **off**.
Up is the opposite of **down**.

Draw lines to match the antonyms.

give	slow
after	small
large	before
old	none
fast	take
all	new
hot	over
under	cold

Antonyms

Write the antonyms.

pull sit top out sad wrong last

1. in   _____

2. bottom _____

3. happy   _____

4. first   _____

5. stand   _____

6. push   _____

7. right   _____

Think of your own antonyms.

_____ is the opposite of _____ .

Write the synonyms and antonyms.

words	synonyms	antonyms
glad	_____	_____
noisy	_____	_____
little	_____	_____
quick	_____	_____

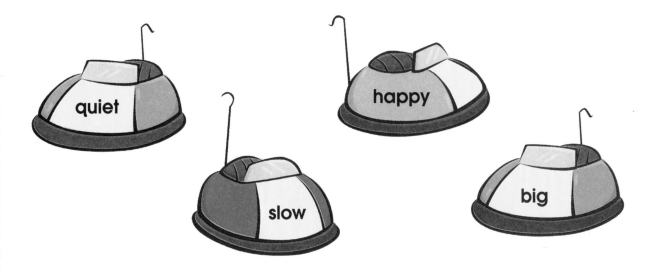

Synonyms and Antonyms

Draw lines to connect the synonyms.

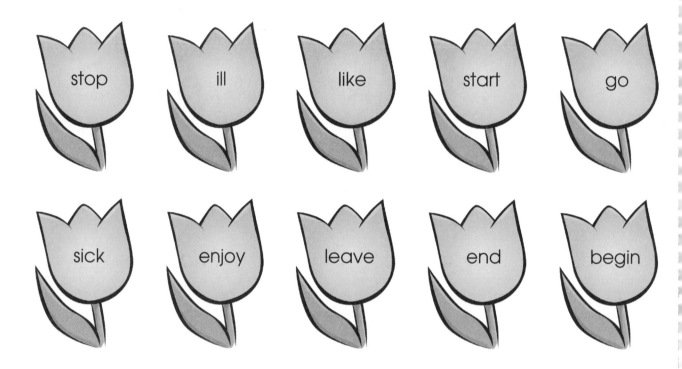

Draw lines to connect the antonyms.

HOMOPHONES

Homophones are words that sound alike but are spelled differently. They also have different meanings.

Write the correct homophones to finish the sentences.

1. Give the toy _____ the baby.

   to   two

2. Put the book over _____ .

   their   there

3. I cannot _____ her.

   hear   here

4. Who _____ the game?

   won   one

5. Is your answer _____ ?

   write   right

6. Jan _____ the apple.

   eight   ate

Homophones

Write the correct homophones to finish the sentences.

one two right see won to write sea

1. I went _____ the store to buy _____ apples.

2. You can _____ fish when you swim in the _____ .

3. _____ time, my dad _____ a prize at the fair.

4. I know I can _____ the _____ word in the blank.

Use the clues to solve the puzzle.

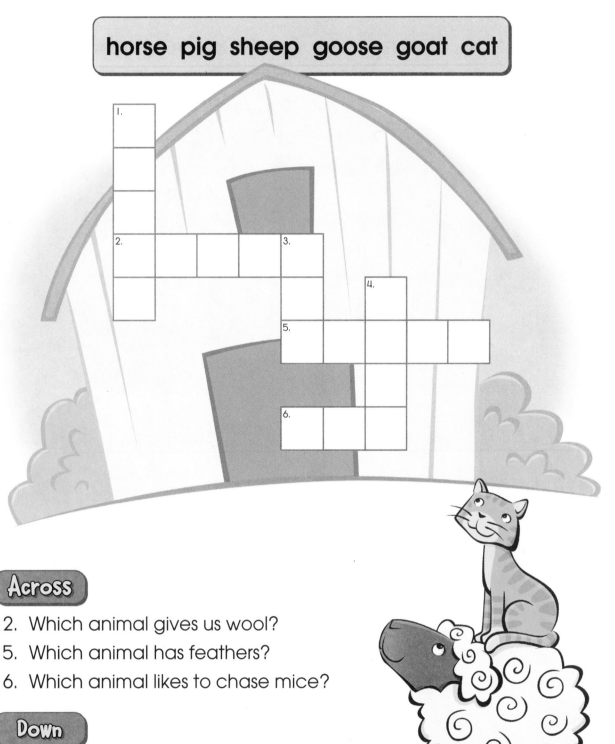

horse pig sheep goose goat cat

Across

2. Which animal gives us wool?
5. Which animal has feathers?
6. Which animal likes to chase mice?

Down

1. Which animal do we ride?
3. Which animal likes to roll in mud?
4. Which animal has horns?

Crossword Puzzle

NIFTY NUMBERS

Use the clues to solve the puzzle.

nine seven three four six five eight

Across

2. Which number comes between four and six?
3. Which number is three plus three?
4. Which number is one more than two?
5. Which number is one less than nine?

Down

1. Which number is one more than eight?
2. Which number is two plus two?
3. Which number is between six and eight?

Crossword Puzzle

Read the sentences.
Circle the correct answers.

1. The clown wears a silly hat.

   yes   no

2. He has a red nose.

   yes   no

3. He has little shoes.

   yes   no

4. He wears a yellow coat.

   yes   no

5. He has two green balls.

   yes   no

6. He rides a bike.

   yes   no

Picture Clues

Read the sentences.
Circle the correct answers.

1. The magician is wearing a tall hat.

   yes   no

2. He is wearing a purple cape.

   yes   no

3. He has a magic wand.

   yes   no

4. He is wearing a red tie.

   yes   no

5. He has little shoes.

   yes   no

6. There is a rabbit in his hat.

   yes   no

Draw lines from the sentences to the correct shoes.

1. These are for snow.

2. These are for puddles.

3. These are for babies.

4. These are for running.

5. These are for clowns.

6. These are for bedtime.

Picture Clues/Logic

DON'T BE SILLY!

Read the sentences and questions.
Write the correct answers on the lines.

> **birds chickens ducks frogs dogs**

1. Cows do not bark. Which animals bark?

   _____

2. Chickens do not quack. Which animals quack?

   _____

3. Dogs do not lay eggs. Which animals lay eggs?

   _____

4. Pigs do not hop. Which animals hop?

   _____

5. Cats do not fly. Which animals fly?

   _____

Read the clues.
Write the names under the correct pictures.

1. Henry keeps the animals homes clean.
2. Liz helps sick animals.
3. Chan works with the sea animals.
4. Beth feeds hungry animals.

_____

_____   _____

Picture Clues/Logic

WHO'S WHO?

Read the clues.
Write the names under the correct pictures.

1. Lisa rides her bike.
2. Chris likes to skate.
3. Jon likes to jog.
4. Anna walks her dog.
5. Pete likes to read.

_____

_____

_____

_____

Read the clues.
Write the names under the correct pictures.

1. Sarah has a green hat.
2. Mia always wears red.
3. Ken never wears blue.
4. Ty has purple shoes.
5. Mimi likes to paint.

Picture Clues/Logic

Read the clues.
Write the names under the correct pictures.

1. Sue likes to wear flip-flops.
2. Eddie always wears a baseball cap.
3. Rachel has freckles.
4. Pedro wears glasses.
5. Beth likes to wear a backpack.

Read the clues.
Write the names under the correct pictures.

1. Jill plays the violin.
2. Zeke plays baseball.
3. Jessie likes to swim.
4. Peter plays soccer.
5. Adam makes things.

_____

_____

_____

_____

Picture Clues/Logic

Read the clues.
Write the names under the correct pictures.

1. Jenna has a dog.
2. Maisy has a cat.
3. Matt has a rabbit.
4. Dan has a turtle.
5. Julian doesn't have a pet.

Read the clues to find the correct answers.

1. Jenny's cat is orange.
   He is wearing a blue collar.
   Circle Jenny's cat.

2. Jack's dog is standing.
   She has spots.
   Circle Jack's dog.

3. The bird's name ends with **y**.
   It has five letters.
   Circle the bird's name.

   Ginger   Billy

   Chipper   Shelly

Logic

Read the clues to solve the problems.
Write the names under the correct pictures.

1. Alexis, Ted, and Kelly had a race.
   Ted came in last place.
   Alexis did not win.

_____   _____   _____

Who won the race? _____

2. John, David, and Rebecca live in these houses.
   John does not live next to David.
   David's house in next to the street sign.

_____   _____   _____

Who lives in the middle house? _____

Logic

Read the poem. Circle the answers to the questions.

I know a silly man who walks on his hands.
He has a silly car. It doesn't go far.
In his silly town, shops are upside down.
Tell me if you can, when you see this silly man.

1. Which is the silly man?

2. Which car would be his?

3. Which hat would be his?

4. Which pet would be his?

Logic

Read the clues. Mark the chart with ✓s.
The first one is done for you.

1. Everyone had fruit.
2. Mom had a salad.
3. Mom, Ben, and Katie had juice.
4. Dad and Ben had a taco.
5. Katie had a turkey sandwich.
6. Dad had milk.

	milk	juice	fruit	salad	taco	sandwich
Dad			✓			
Ben			✓			
Mom			✓			
Katie			✓			

Write the names under the correct pictures.

_____

_____

_____

_____

Logic ©School Zone Publishing Company

Use the clues to solve the puzzle.

toast boat gold goat hole note

Across

2. made with bread
4. an animal
6. short letter

Down

1. moves in water
3. an empty space
5. a yellow metal

Crossword Puzzle

FLAVORFUL FRUITS

Use the clues to solve the puzzle.

orange grapes pear lemon banana apple

Across

1. I am a color.
3. I am long and yellow.
5. I rhyme with "bear".
6. I am used to make a tart drink.

Down

2. I grow in bunches.
4. I make a good pie.

The bugs at your picnic have a message for you.
Use the code to find the message.

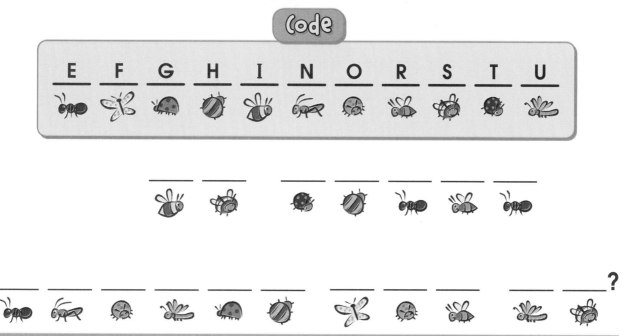

Check the boxes next to the bugs that are insects.

Insect Basics

3 Body Parts:
1. head
2. thorax
3. abdomen

Antennae

Most have wings.

6 Legs

Decoding

Use the code to answer the questions.

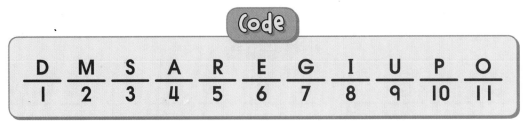

Code

D	M	S	A	R	E	G	I	U	P	O
1	2	3	4	5	6	7	8	9	10	11

1. Which deer is the largest?

The ___ ___ ___ ___ ___
    2   11 11 3   6

2. Which animal plays dead to avoid attack?

The ___ ___ ___ ___ ___ ___ ___
   11 10 11 3   3   9   2

3. Which animal barks like a dog when frightened?

The ___ ___ ___ ___ ___ ___ ___   ___ ___ ___
   10 5   4   8   5   8   6   1 11 7

Write the problem numbers in the boxes by the correct animals.

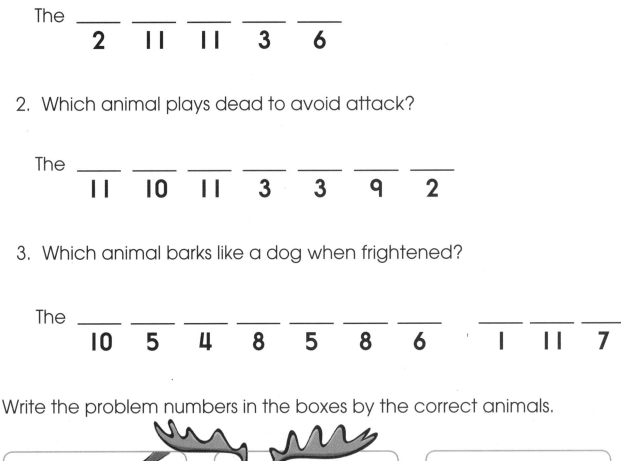

Use the code to answer the questions.

Code

F	Y	L	A	I	U	T	S	E	R	P	H	N
1	2	3	4	5	6	7	8	9	10	11	12	13

1. Which creature can jump 200 times its own height?

   The ___ ___ ___ ___
       1   3   9   4

2. Which animal has a bad reputation for attacking creatures in the water?

   The ___ ___ ___ ___ ___ ___ ___
       11   5 10   4 13 12   4

3. Which mammal lays eggs instead of giving birth to live young?

   The ___ ___ ___ ___ ___ ___ ___ ___
       11   3   4   7   2 11   6   8

Write the problem numbers in the boxes by the correct animals.

Decoding

Use the code to answer the questions.

Code

R	T	E	U	O	A	S	H	I	C	B	X	L
1	2	3	4	5	6	7	8	9	10	11	12	13

1. Which bird is the largest?

The ___ ___ ___ ___ ___ ___ ___
    5   7   2   1   9 10 8

2. Which animal runs the fastest?

The ___ ___ ___ ___ ___ ___ ___
   10 8 3 3 2 6 8

3. Which sea animal can live over 100 years?

The ___ ___ ___ ___ ___ ___ ___ ___ ___
   7 3 6 2 4 1 2 13 3

Write the problem numbers in the boxes by the correct animals.

Decoding   ©School Zone Publishing Company

ANIMAL FACTS

Use the code to answer the questions.

Code

P	O	S	F	Y	N	I	L	T	E	G	W	R	A
1	2	3	4	5	6	7	8	9	10	11	12	13	14

1. Which animal travels on one big foot?

The ____ ____ ____ ____ ____
      3   6   14   7   8

2. Which wild dog is the largest?

The ____ ____ ____ ____   ____ ____ ____ ____
      11   13   14   5   12   2   8   4

3. Which bird can be taught to use words?

The ____ ____ ____ ____ ____ ____
      1   14   13   13   2   9

Write the problem numbers in the boxes by the correct animals.

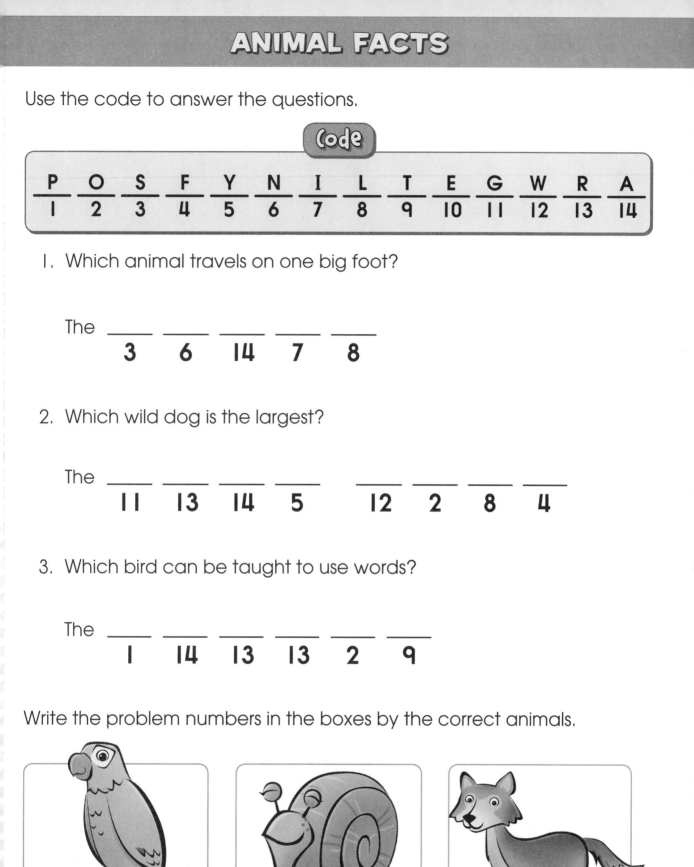

    Decoding

Use the code to answer the questions.

Code

W	F	H	I	L	G	A	N	U	B	E	T	R	P
1	2	3	4	5	6	7	8	9	10	11	12	13	14

1. Which animal is the largest?

The ___ ___ ___ ___   ___ ___ ___ ___ ___
    10 5   9   11   1   3   7   5   11

2. Which animal is the tallest?

The ___ ___ ___ ___ ___ ___ ___
    6   4   13 7   2   2   11

3. Which land animal is the largest?

The ___ ___ ___ ___ ___ ___ ___ ___
    11 5   11 14 3   7   8   12

Write the problem numbers in the boxes by the correct animals.

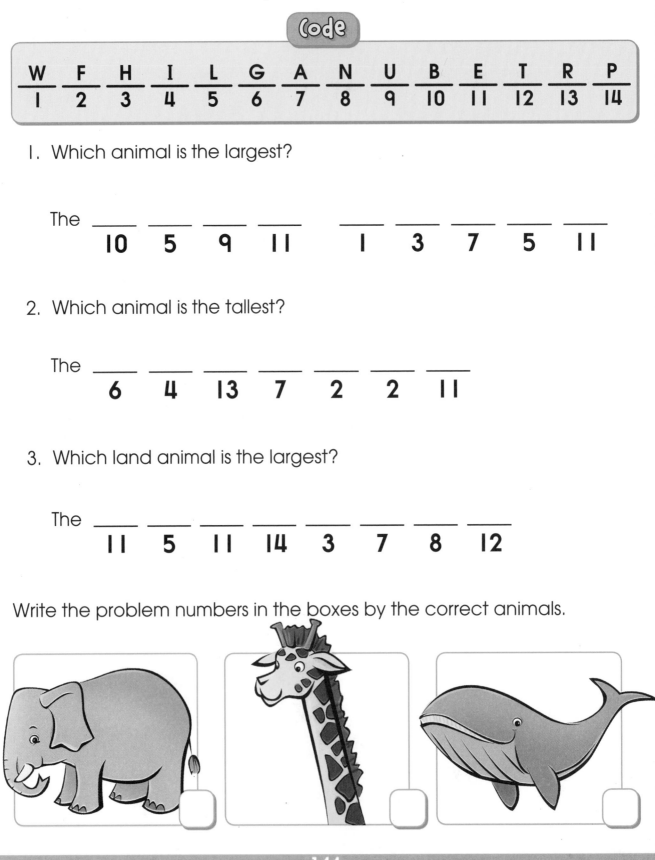

Decoding

FORWARD AND BACKWARD

Use the code to write words for the clues.

The word will read the same forward and backward.

Code

A	B	D	E	I	M	N	O	P	R	S	T	U	Y
1	2	3	4	5	6	7	8	9	10	11	12	13	14

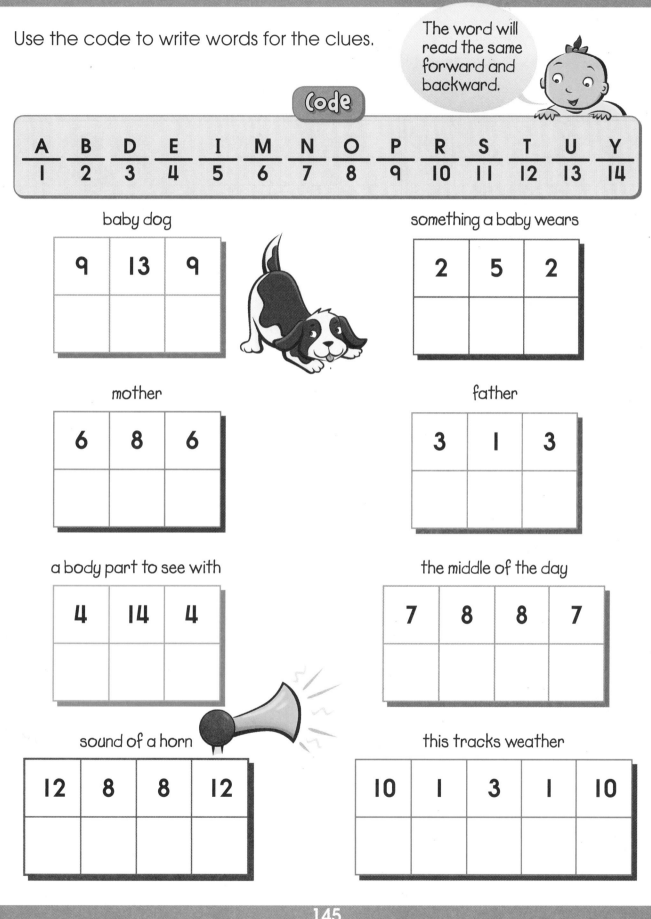

baby dog

9	13	9

something a baby wears

2	5	2

mother

6	8	6

father

3	1	3

a body part to see with

4	14	4

the middle of the day

7	8	8	7

sound of a horn

12	8	8	12

this tracks weather

10	1	3	1	10

Decoding/Palindromes

Your friends have left you a note on the beach.
Use the code to find the message.

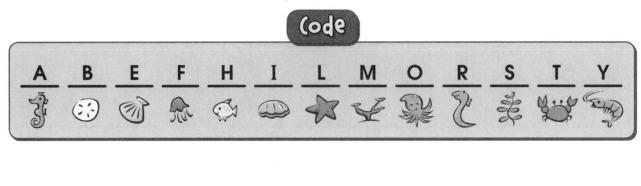

SAY THIS

THREE TIMES

FAST:

SHE SELLS

SEASHELLS BY

THE SEASHORE!

ARE YOU READY?

Use the clues to solve the puzzle.

letter bird turn mother word hurt work

Across

3. to move around a center
4. to do harm
5. something that is said
6. an animal with wings and feathers

Down

1. a note written to a person
2. a female parent
5. job

Crossword Puzzle

IN OTHER WORDS

Use the clues to solve the puzzle.

think when chop shut
thin   where check shop

Across

1. to close
2. to cut into pieces
3. to use the mind
4. at what time

Down

1. a store
2. to test if true
3. slim
4. at what place

Alphabetical order is a way of arranging words to follow the same sequence as the letters in the alphabet.
Use the first letters of the words to put them in alphabetical order.

ant   **c**at   **p**ig

The words dig, dog, and day begin with the same first letter.
Use their second letters to put them in alphabetical order.

d**a**y   d**i**g   d**o**g

Put the names of these friends in alphabetical order.

1. Lucy, Tina, Beth

   _____   _____   _____

2. Peter, Matt, Jamie

   _____   _____   _____

3. Amy, Abby, Anna

   _____   _____   _____

4. David, Drew, Doug

   _____   _____   _____

Alphabetical Order

The amusement park opens today!
From 1-6, number the names in alphabetical order.

FUN City

Ferris Wheel

3 Roller Coaster

1 Bumper Cars

2 Log Ride

3 Carousel

Wave Pool

Which is your favorite ride? _____

Alphabetical Order

©School Zone Publishing Company

THE FARMER'S MARKET

Write the names in alphabetical order.
Write numbers to tell how many there are.

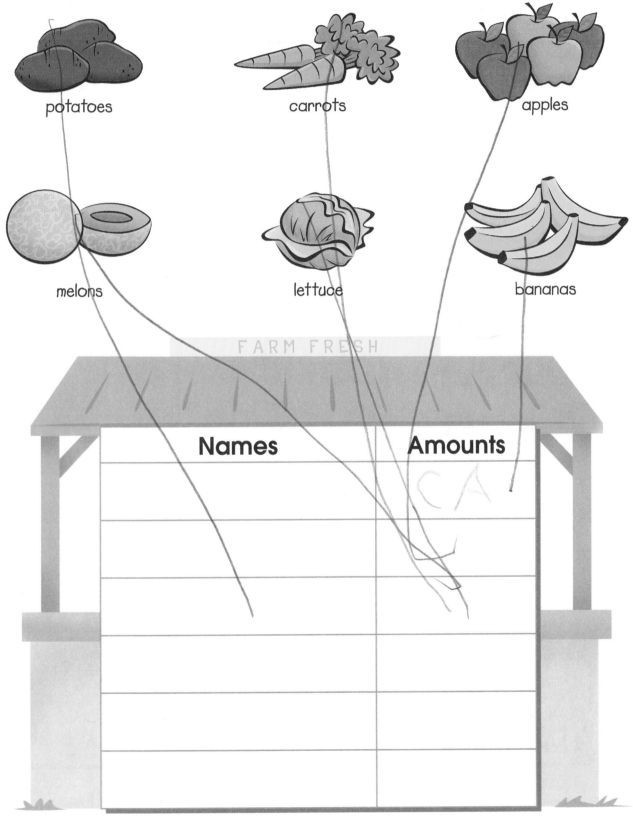

potatoes

carrots

apples

melons

lettuce

bananas

FARM FRESH

Names	Amounts

Alphabetical Order/Counting

SORTING THE BOOKSHELF

Use the authors' last names to number the books in alphabetical order.

1. Snake Hunt by H. S. Fang — [3]

   Cub Kitchen by Ted E. Bear — [1]

   Cats and Dogs by Red Setter — [3]

2. Racing for Fun by Howie Fast — [1]

   Home Run! by Ima Hitter — [2]

   Gymnastics by Flip N. Jump — [ ]

3. Mountain Trail by Oma Blisters — [1]

   Jungle Trek by Annie Body — [2]

   Desert Heat by Sandy Beach — [2]

152

Use the code to solve the riddle.
The first letter is done for you.

Code

	1	2	3	4	5
☀	S	T	U	O	L
🌙	W	B	X	K	B
🌈	N	U	E	D	K
❄	L	Z	P	G	D
🌧	A	R	Y	I	C

Which animal never needs a haircut?

1 🌧	2 🌙	1 🌧	1 ❄	4 🌈	3 🌈	1 🌧	4 ❄	5 ☀	3 🌈
A	W	A	L	N	N	A	L	S	N

Decoding Puzzle

Use the code to answer the question.

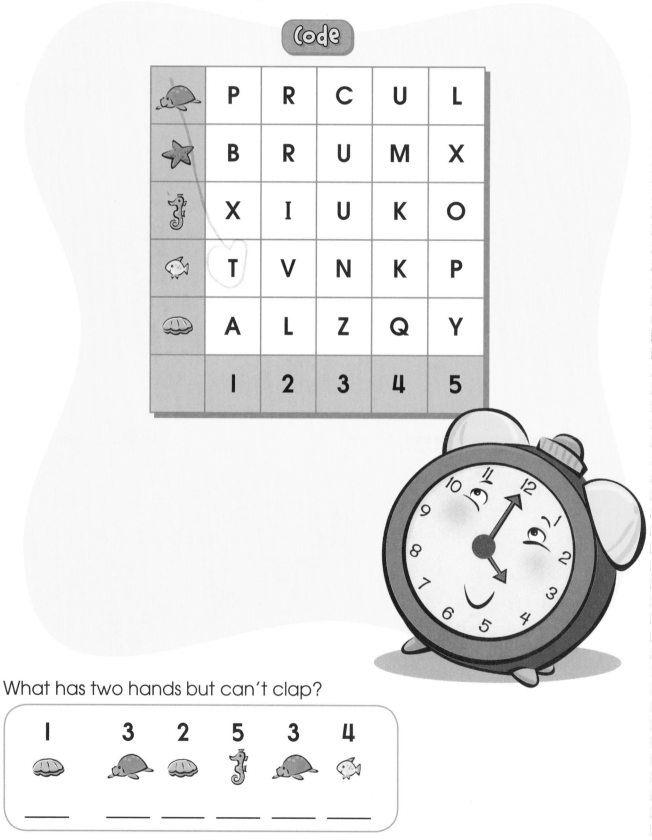

Code

	1	2	3	4	5
turtle	P	R	C	U	L
star	B	R	U	M	X
seahorse	X	I	U	K	O
fish	T	V	N	K	P
shell	A	L	Z	Q	Y

What has two hands but can't clap?

1	3	2	5	3	4
shell	turtle	shell	seahorse	turtle	fish
___	___	___	___	___	___

154

1. Circle the things you can wear.

2. Circle the things you can eat.

3. Circle the things that are alive.

4. Circle the things you can ride.

5. Circle the things you can hear.

Analysis/Classification

1. Underline the things that hop.

2. Underline the things you can smell.

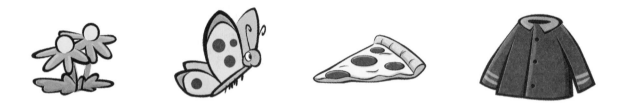

3. Underline the things that fly.

4. Underline the things we use in winter.

5. Underline the farm animals.

1. Circle the things you can eat.
   Underline the things you can wear.

2. Underline the animals that are pets.
   Circle the animal that lives in water.

3. Cross out the pictures whose names rhyme.
   Circle the number.

4. Underline the pictures whose names begin with the letter **b**.
   Cross out the zoo animal.

Analysis/Classification

Circle the items that go with summer.

boots sweaters

shorts swimsuits

T-shirts sunglasses

sandals watermelons

beach towels picnic baskets

Circle the items that go with winter.

scarves coats

swimsuits boots

mittens snow pants

earmuffs sandals

stocking caps snowmen

Analysis/Classification ©School Zone Publishing Company

TIC-TAC-TOE

Find the words that go together.
Look across, down, and diagonally.

1

gate	over	snip
gave	under	chain
ripe	above	chair

2

baseball	smaller	found
tallest	soccer	happy
bumpy	short	football

3

cloud	hilly	rain
claw	beak	wing
hose	nose	coin

4

first	flower	summer
frost	spring	lamp
winter	hand	sand

Analysis/Classification

TIC-TAC-TOE

Find the words that go together.
Look across, down, and diagonally.

1

fish	key	five
bug	jump	four
star	blue	two

2

ball	rain	bat
lemon	butterfly	green
robin	down	red

3

sun	big	goat
wet	rain	two
star	old	snow

4

rose	ant	red
fox	bus	ten
dollar	penny	nickel

Analysis/Classification

Find the words that go together.
Look across, down, and diagonally.

1

bee	ant	fly
seal	hat	frog
house	ball	blue

2

yo-yo	bird	one
hand	ball	hill
soap	gate	doll

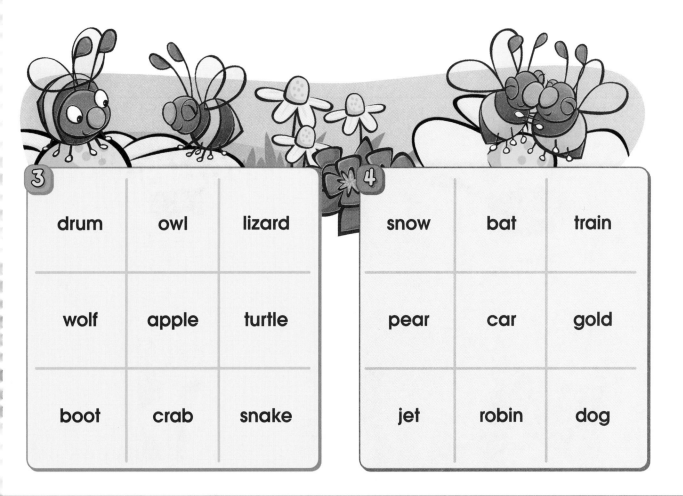

3

drum	owl	lizard
wolf	apple	turtle
boot	crab	snake

4

snow	bat	train
pear	car	gold
jet	robin	dog

Analysis/Classification

Cross out what you do not need.

1. To catch a fish, you need:

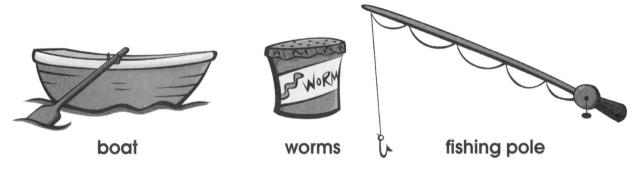

boat   **worms**   **fishing pole**

2. To make a birdhouse, you need:

birdseed   **nails**   **boards**

3. To cook an egg, you need:

pan   **sink**   **stove**

4. To see a movie, you need:

money   **tickets**   **popcorn**

Prior Knowledge/Analysis

Cross out what you do not need.

1. To play baseball, you need:

bat

cap

ball

2. To wash your dog, you need:

food dish

soap

water

3. To write a letter, you need:

paper

stamp

pencil

4. To brush your teeth, you need:

hairbrush

toothpaste

toothbrush

Prior Knowledge/Analysis

ANIMAL FACTS

Some animals protect themselves in unusual ways.
Write the correct names to finish the sentences.

lizard porcupine turtle armadillo cheetah squid

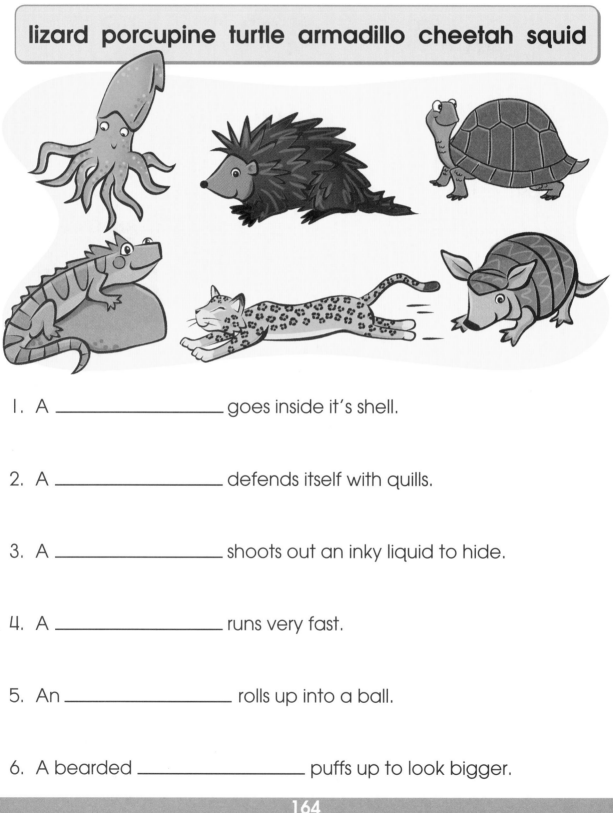

1. A _____ goes inside it's shell.

2. A _____ defends itself with quills.

3. A _____ shoots out an inky liquid to hide.

4. A _____ runs very fast.

5. An _____ rolls up into a ball.

6. A bearded _____ puffs up to look bigger.

Write the correct names under the clues.

> **zebra elephant horse raccoon wolf giraffe**

1. It carries a trunk.

   _____

2. A cowboy rides one.

   _____

3. It looks like a horse with stripes.

   _____

4. It scared Little Red Riding Hood.

   _____

5. It looks like it is wearing a mask.

   _____

6. It has the longest neck.

   _____

Prior Knowledge/Analysis

NURSERY RHYMES

Jack be nimble,
Jack be quick,
Jack jump over
The candlestick.

Hickory, dickory, dock,
The mouse ran up the clock.
The clock struck one,
The mouse ran down,
Hickory, dickory, dock.

Mary had a little lamb,
whose fleece was white as snow.
And everywhere that Mary went,
the lamb was sure to go.

Peter, Peter, pumpkin eater,
Had a wife but couldn't keep her;
He put her in a pumpkin shell,
And there he kept her very well.

Rub-a-dub-dub,
Three men in a tub,
And who do you think they may be?
The butcher, the baker,
The candlestick maker,
Turn them out, knaves all three.

The itsy bitsy spider went up the waterspout.
Down came the rain, and washed the spider out.
Up came the sun, and dried up all the rain,
and the itsy bitsy spider went up the spout again.

Nursery Rhyme Refresher
©School Zone Publishing Company

Read the questions.
Write the correct answers.

> ## Mary Peter spider Jack mouse three

1. What ran up the clock?

   _____

2. Who had a little lamb?

   _____

3. What went up the waterspout?

   _____

4. Who eats pumpkins?

   _____

5. How many men were in a tub?

   _____

6. Who jumped over a candlestick?

   _____

Analysis

Read the sentences. Circle yes if they are true. Circle no if they are not true. Circle the letters next to your answers. Then write the circled letters in order on the blanks below to answer the riddle.

1.	All birds have feathers.	yes	y	no	g
2.	All living things need food.	yes	a	no	l
3.	Insects have bones.	yes	w	no	r
4.	Ice is frozen water.	yes	d	no	f
5.	Trees are large plants.	yes	s	no	r
6.	Plants need water to grow.	yes	t	no	s
7.	The world's largest animal is the giraffe.	yes	v	no	i
8.	The earth is flat.	yes	i	no	c
9.	A plant is alive.	yes	k	no	x

What has a foot on each side and one in the middle?

A ___ ___ ___ ___ ___ ___ ___

Read the sentences. Circle yes if they are true. Circle no if they are not true. Circle the letters next to your answers. Then write the circled letters in order on the blanks below to answer the riddle.

1. Celery is a vegetable.	yes	o	no	g
2. Birds fly.	yes	i	no	j
3. The letters **a**, **e**, **i**, **o**, and **u** are consonants.	yes	s	no	n
4. "Each", "eat", and "bead" have the **long a** sound.	yes	w	no	k
5. "Happy" is the opposite of "sad".	yes	m	no	r
6. Bees make honey.	yes	e	no	l
7. "Same" is a synonym of "different".	yes	k	no	n
8. "King" and "ring" are rhyming words.	yes	t	no	q

What do you give sick pigs?

____ ____ ____ ____ ____ ____ ____ ____

Prior Knowledge/Analysis

Read the sentences. Circle yes if they are true. Circle no if they are not true. Circle the letters next to your answers. Then write the circled letters in order on the blanks below to answer the riddle.

1.	A butterfly is an insect.	yes	p	no	j
2.	Most fish hatch from eggs.	yes	r	no	k
3.	People visit zoos to see plants.	yes	s	no	o
4.	Your heart pumps blood around the body.	yes	b	no	u
5.	Lizards are a kind of insect.	yes	g	no	l
6.	Birds lay eggs.	yes	e	no	x
7.	Insects have eight legs.	yes	t	no	m
8.	Tadpoles are young frogs or toads.	yes	s	no	f

What did the math book say to the storybook?
I've got a lot of _____ .

_____ _____ _____ _____ _____ _____ _____ _____

Read the sentences. Circle yes if they are true. Circle no if they are not true. Circle the letters next to your answers. Then write the circled letters in order on the blanks below to answer the riddle.

1.	There are four seasons in a year.	yes	c	no	x
2.	A city is smaller than a town.	yes	p	no	a
3.	Neighbors live far apart.	yes	d	no	l
4.	All states have a capital city.	yes	e	no	k
5.	911 is a phone number to call for emergency help.	yes	n	no	h
6.	Lakes are larger than ponds.	yes	d	no	v
7.	The top of most maps is north.	yes	a	no	s
8.	Temperature is the measure of heat.	yes	r	no	h

What shows the month and days of the year?

A ____ ____   ____ ____ ____ ____ ____   ____ ____ ____

Prior Knowledge/Analysis

Read the sentences. Circle yes if they are true. Circle no if they are not true. Circle the letters next to your answers. Then write the circled letters in order on the blanks below to answer the riddle.

1.	Clouds are made of tiny drops of water.	yes	r	no	y
2.	You can see air.	yes	o	no	a
3.	You hear thunder before you see lightning.	yes	u	no	i
4.	Moving air is wind.	yes	n	no	j
5.	Lightning can cause a snowstorm.	yes	k	no	b
6.	Rain and snow fall from the clouds.	yes	o	no	v
7.	Earth gets heat from the sun.	yes	w	no	s
8.	Air is found only outside.	yes	l	no	s

What are the bows of color sometimes seen in the sky after rain?

____ ____ ____ ____ ____ ____ ____

Prior Knowledge/Analysis

SOUNDS FISHY

Use the code to solve the riddle.

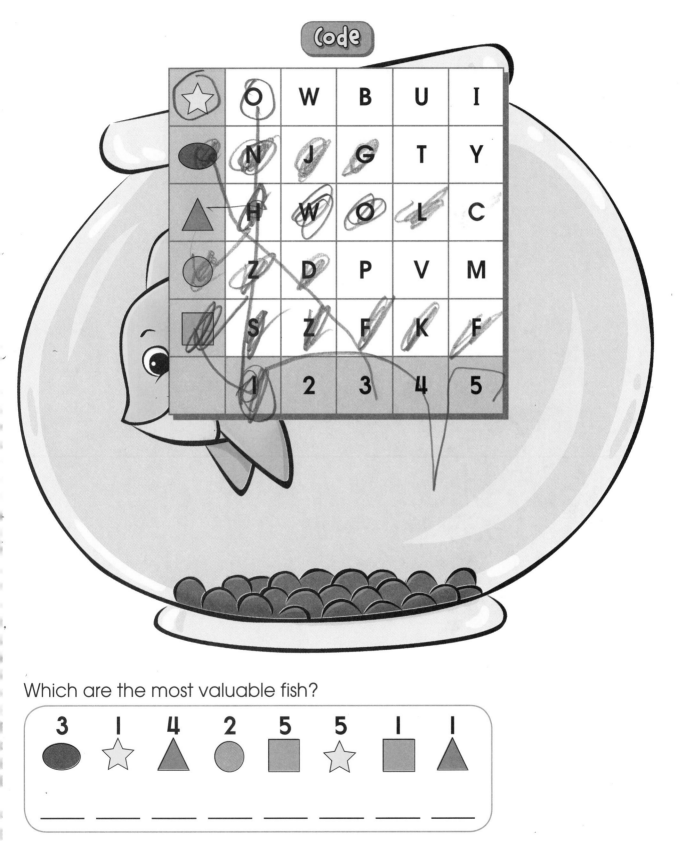

Code

	1	2	3	4	5
☆	O	W	B	U	I
⬭	N	J	G	T	Y
▲	H	W	O	L	C
⬤	Z	D	P	V	M
◻	S	Z	F	K	F

Which are the most valuable fish?

3	1	4	2	5	5	1	1
⬭	☆	▲	⬤	◻	☆	◻	▲

_____ _____ _____ _____ _____ _____ _____ _____

Decoding Puzzle

Use the code to solve the riddle.

Code

★	W	L	X	R	E
⬭	I	A	P	H	Q
▲	M	N	L	V	K
●	E	D	Y	Z	P
■	C	L	D	B	H
	I	2	3	4	5

What do you call an insect born in May?

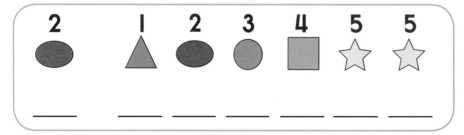

2	I	2	3	4	5	5
⬭	▲	⬭	●	■	★	★

___ ___ ___ ___ ___ ___ ___

Decoding Puzzle　　　　　　　　©School Zone Publishing Company

BIRTHDAY PARTY

Write 1 by what happens first.
Write 2 by what happens next.
Write 3 by what happens last.

1   2   3

1   1   3

Story Order

Number the pictures from 1 to 6 to show the correct order.

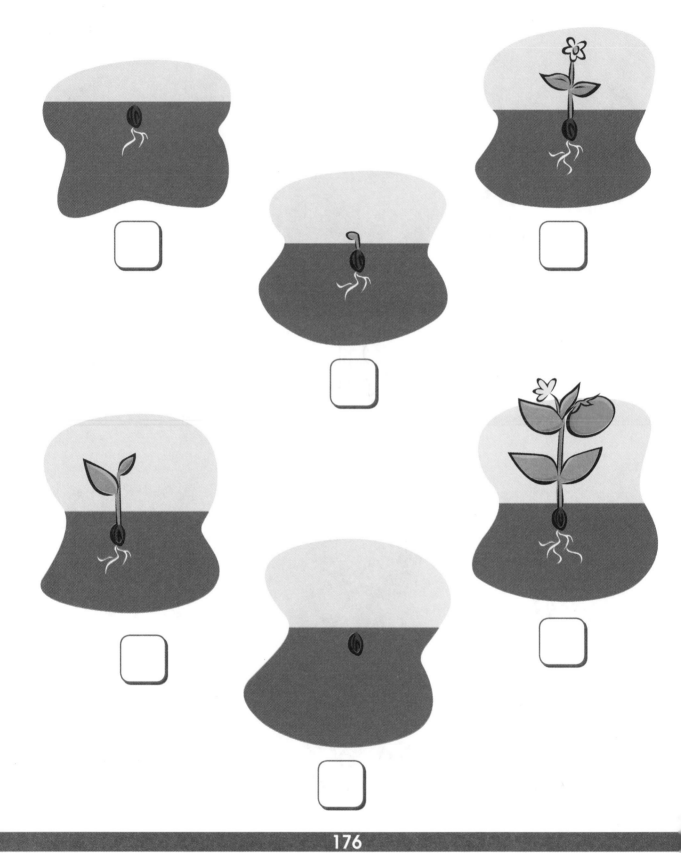

Story Order   ©School Zone Publishing Company

Number the pictures from 1 to 6 to show the correct order.

Story Order

Number the pictures from 1 to 6 to show the correct order.

©School Zone Publishing Company

OH CHRISTMAS TREE!

Number the pictures from 1 to 6 to show the correct order.

Story Order

TAKING A TRIP

Write 1 by what happens first.
Write 2 by what happens next.
Write 3 by what happens last.

1. Write what happened at the beginning.

First Pas the girl to gef tne tick

2. Write what happened in the middle.

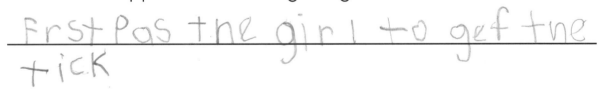

3. Write what happened at the end.

Write 1 by what happens first.
Write 2 by what happens next.
Write 3 by what happens last.

1. Write what happened at the beginning.

_____

2. Write what happened in the middle.

_____

3. Write what happened at the end.

_____

Story Order

Read the stories.
Number the pictures from 1 to 3 to show the correct order.

1. The duck went to a party.
   The duck ate some cake.
   The duck went home.

_____   _____   _____

2. Mom made a cake.
   I ate a piece.
   Then I went to bed.

_____   _____   _____

3. Jane sees a duck.
   The duck sees Jane.
   Then the duck walks up to Jane.

_____   _____   _____

Story Order

Read the stories.
Number the pictures from 1 to 3 to show the correct order.

1. Tracy pulls her wagon.
   She finds a kitten.
   Tracy gives the kitten a ride.

2. Tom has an old wagon.
   "I will paint my wagon," says Tom.
   So he paints his wagon.

3. The kitten wants to eat.
   It waits for food.
   At last, the kitten eats.

Story Order

Josh and Dani planned a neighborhood dog wash.
Read the sentences. Draw a line to show where they go.

1. First, they go to Mrs. Green's.
2. Next, they go to Mr. Berry's.
3. After that, they go to the Ride house.
4. Last, they go to Mrs. Ball's.

RIDE

BALL

GREEN

BERRY

Rub-a-dub-dub,
Washing dogs in a tub.
Rub-a-dub-dub,
How many dogs did they scrub?_____ dogs

Story Order/Following Directions

A frog goes through five stages during its life cycle:

1   2   3   4   5

Number the sentences from 1 to 5
to show the correct order.

_____ Froggy is a tiny tadpole.

_____ Froggy is a big frog.

_____ Froggy is an egg.

_____ Froggy grows four legs.

_____ Froggy grows two legs.

Story Order

Here is the life cycle of an apple tree:

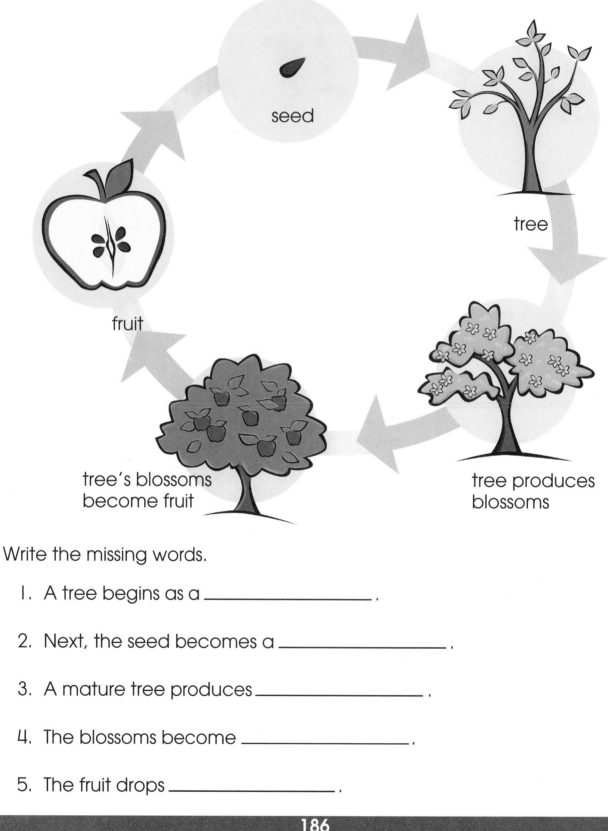

seed

tree

fruit

tree's blossoms become fruit

tree produces blossoms

Write the missing words.

1. A tree begins as a _____ .

2. Next, the seed becomes a _____ .

3. A mature tree produces _____ .

4. The blossoms become _____ .

5. The fruit drops _____ .

A butterfly goes through four stages during its life cycle:

1. egg

2. larva (caterpillar)

3. pupa (chrysalis)

4. adult (butterfly)

During each stage, the insect looks different and lives in a new way. Only the caterpillar and the adult can move about.

Write the missing words.

1. A butterfly begins as an _____.

2. The egg hatches into a _____.

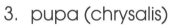

3. The caterpillar turns into a _____.

4. An adult _____ breaks out of the pupa.

Story Order

Read the story.

The night was dark.
Tina heard something go "whooo!"
Tina was scared.
The window blew open.
Tina saw an owl.
The owl went "whooo!"
Tina was not scared then.

Number the sentences from
1 to 4 to show the correct order.

_____The window blew open.

_____Tina saw an owl.

_____Tina was scared.

_____Tina was not scared then.

Read the directions.

Find a place that is sunny.
Dig a hole.
Set the tomato plant in the hole.
Pat dirt around the plant.
Water the plant often.
When the tomatoes are ripe, enjoy!

Number the sentences from
1 to 5 to show the correct order.

_____Set the tomato plant in the hole.

_____Find a place that is sunny.

_____Pat dirt around the plant.

_____Water the plant often.

_____Dig a hole.

189

Can you guess what will happen next?

John received an invitation to a Halloween party. He went to his dad's closet and found some old clothes for his costume. After that, John arrived at the Halloween party.

1. What will happen next?

_____

2. What clues make you think that?

_____

190

Can you guess what will happen next?

Henry was thirsty. He went to the cabinet and got a glass. Then he opened the refrigerator. Next, he got some milk. Henry poured the milk into the glass.

1. What will Henry do next?

_____

2. What clues make you think that?

_____

Story Order/Inference

THE SECRET CAVE

Words like "first", "next", "last", and "then" can help you understand when things happen in a story.

Read the story. Answer the questions.

Gemma wanted to go to the beach.
It was raining, so she had to stay home.
She decided to build a secret cave.
First, she put some chairs in a circle.
Next, she put a large sheet over the chairs.
Finally, she put pillows into the secret cave and crawled inside.
Gemma forgot all about the beach.

1. What was the first thing Gemma did to build the secret cave?

   _____

2. What was the second step in building the secret cave?

   _____

3. What was the last step?

   _____

4. Guess why Gemma was happy when she crawled in the cave.

   _____

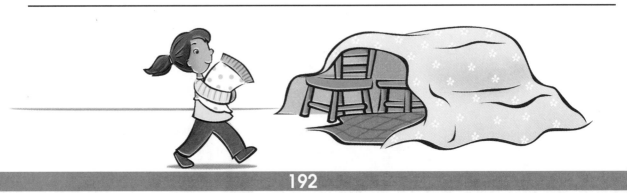

192

Look at the pictures.
Write the names of the pictures in their numbered rows in the puzzle.
Use the code to solve the riddle. An example is done for you.

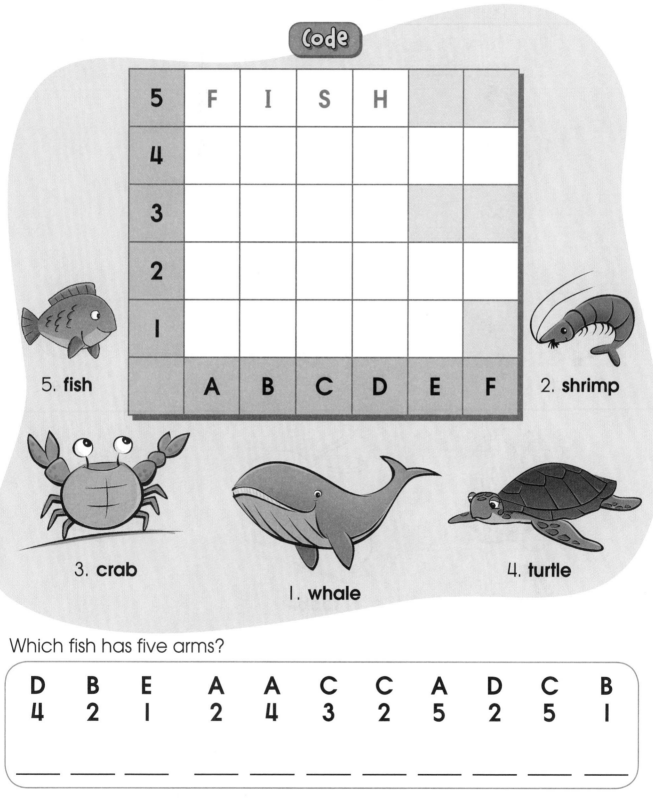

Code

	A	B	C	D	E	F
5	F	I	S	H		
4						
3						
2						
1						

5. fish

2. shrimp

3. crab

1. whale

4. turtle

Which fish has five arms?

D	B	E	A	A	C	C	A	D	C	B
4	2	1	2	4	3	2	5	2	5	1

___ ___ ___ ___ ___ ___ ___ ___ ___ ___ ___

Decoding Puzzle

GARDEN FRIENDS

Look at the pictures.
Write the names of the pictures in their numbered rows in the puzzle.
Use the code to solve the riddle.

Code

	A	B	C	D	E	F
5						
4						
3						
2						
1						

2. bird

4. bee

3. snail

1. rabbit

5. frog

What do you call a snail on a ship?

B	A	B	B	E	E	B	C
1	3	3	1	1	3	4	2

___ ___ ___ ___ ___ ___ ___

REAL OR MAKE-BELIEVE?

Look at the picture.
How many strange things can you find? _____
Circle them.

Real or Make-Believe

Look at the picture.
How many strange things can you find? _____
Circle them.

REAL OR MAKE-BELIEVE?

Real things can actually happen.
Make-believe things cannot really happen.

Circle real or make-believe.

1. The cow jumped over the moon.   real   make-believe

    Jenny fed the cow hay.   real   make-believe

2. The cat looks for mice in the barn.   real   make-believe

    The cat came dancing out of the barn.   real   make-believe

3. An old woman lives near us.   real   make-believe

    An old woman lives in a shoe.   real   make-believe

4. Three little kittens lost their mittens.   real   make-believe

    Three little kittens were lost.   real   make-believe

    Real or Make-Believe

REALITY OR FANTASY?

Reality stories are about things that have or could really happen.
Fantasy stories are about things that could not really happen.

Reality story

Fantasy story

Write **R** in front of what could really happen.
Write **F** in front of what could not really happen.

_____ 1. The pig spread his wings and flew away.

_____ 2. The fireman rushed to put out the fire.

_____ 3. The fox had a party with the chicken.

_____ 4. Sea turtles laid their eggs on the beach.

_____ 5. The dish ran away with the spoon.

_____ 6. The farmer planted gumball trees.

_____ 7. Dad rowed the boat across the river.

_____ 8. The baby played with toy animals.

Many stories are about make-believe animals.
Read the story.

Cookie is a cat. Cookie likes cooking.
Cookie cooks what he likes to eat.

Cookie cooks cake. He cooks it from fish.
Cookie cooks pie from fish, too.
Cookie even cooks cookies from fish!

Circle the correct answers.

1. What is the best name for the story?

   Real Cats   Eating Cookies   A Cat That Cooks

2. What does Cookie use to make everything he cooks?

   cookies   pie   fish   cake

3. What kind of animal is Cookie?

   a real cow   a make-believe cow

   a real cat   a make-believe cat

4. Can real cats cook?   yes   no

5. Do real cats like to eat fish?   yes   no

6. Is Cookie a real cat?   yes   no

Real or Make-Believe

CHRISTMAS FRIEND

Use the code to solve the riddle.

Code

☆	U	E	B	R	Q	M
⬭	R	U	G	I	H	J
▲	J	X	F	L	N	R
●	E	V	S	C	A	D
■	K	T	Z	O	P	E
	1	2	3	4	5	6

Which animal drops from the sky?

5 ●   6 ▲   5 ●   4 ⬭   5 ▲   6 ●   2 ☆   6 ■   1 ⬭

___ ___ ___ ___ ___ - ___ ___ ___

Decoding Puzzle

©School Zone Publishing Company

Use the code to solve the riddle.

Code

	1	2	3	4	5	6
★	O	T	J	L	U	B
⬭	U	Q	P	B	L	B
△	R	S	K	O	A	D
◯	B	P	L	I	Z	X
▢	N	M	A	H	E	B

What is easy to get into, but hard to get out of?

2	1	4	5	6	3	5
★	△	△	★	⬭	◯	▢

_____ _____ _____ _____ _____ _____ _____

201

Decoding Puzzle

FACT OR OPINION?

A **fact** is something that can be proved.

Birds have wings.
You can look at a bird or check in a book to find out whether birds have wings.

An **opinion** is something that someone believes. An opinion can't be proved.

A robin is pretty.

Circle fact or opinion.

1. Most birds can fly.   fact   opinion

2. Birds make good pets.   fact   opinion

3. Birds lay eggs.   fact   opinion

4. Owls are smart.   fact   opinion

5. Robins make the best nests.   fact   opinion

6. Most birds have feathers.   fact   opinion

Extra Credit!

Write one fact about birds.

_____

What is your opinion about birds?

_____

Circle fact or opinion.

1. Spiders have eight legs.   fact   opinion

2. Insects are scary.   fact   opinion

3. I would love to have a pet tarantula.   fact   opinion

4. Insects have three body parts.   fact   opinion

5. Both spiders and insects shed their skin.   fact   opinion

6. Insects are better than spiders.   fact   opinion

Extra Credit!

Write one fact about spiders.

_____

What is your opinion about insects?

_____

Fact or Opinion

Circle fact or opinion.

1. Most ocean animals are fish.   fact   opinion

2. Fish make good pets.   fact   opinion

3. Some fish have bright colors.   fact   opinion

4. Fish are cold-blooded.   fact   opinion

5. Fishing is fun.   fact   opinion

6. Everyone should eat fish.   fact   opinion

Extra Credit!

Write one fact about fish.

_____

What is your opinion about fish?

_____

Use the code to solve the riddle.

Code

	1	2	3	4	5	6
☆	O	I	Y	W	L	R
⬤	R	E	D	B	G	C
△	K	X	F	D	H	J
◯	L	A	C	K	S	M
◼	M	Q	O	N	T	R

Which month has 28 days?

2	5	1	1	3	5	5	2	6
◯	☆	◯	☆	△	◼	△	⬤	◯

_____ _____ _____ _____ _____ _____ _____ _____ _____

205

Decoding Puzzle

Look at the pictures.
Write the names of the pictures in their numbered rows in the puzzle.
Use the code to solve the riddle.

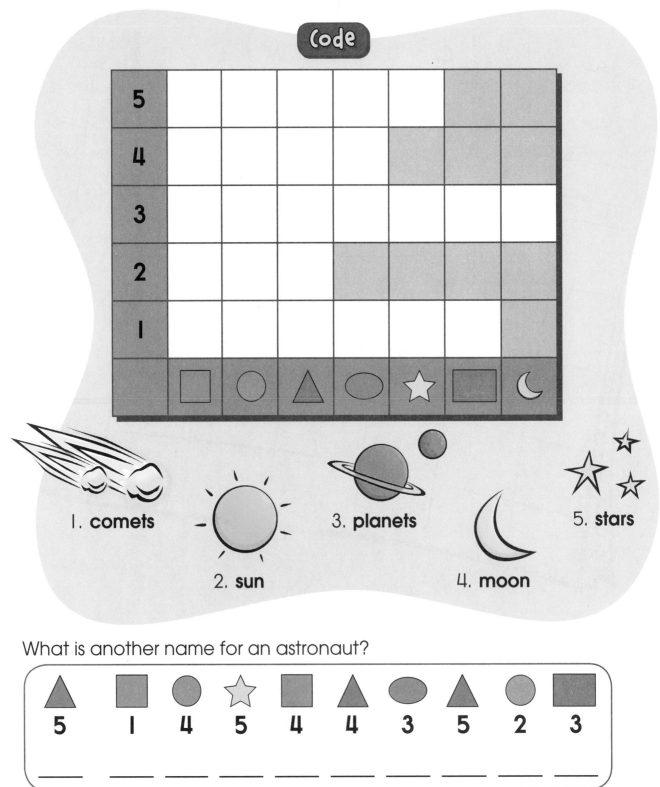

Code

1. comets
2. sun
3. planets
4. moon
5. stars

What is another name for an astronaut?

△	◻	●	☆	◻	△	⬭	△	●	◻
5	1	4	5	4	4	3	5	2	3

__ __ __ __ __ __ __ __ __ __

Keegan is at the store with her mom.
Use the picture to answer the questions.

1. Can yogurt be found in the dairy section?   yes   no

2. Are vegetables to the left of proteins?   yes   no

3. Can bread be found in the fruit section?   yes   no

Reading Maps

CAMPING OUT

Dani and Josh went on a family camping trip.
Use the map to answer the questions.

1. A camper is by the playground.   yes   no

2. There is a path to the lake.   yes   no

3. The hiking trail is near the camp store.   yes   no

Reading Maps   ©School Zone Publishing Company

Campers Only

Camp
Playground

Picnic
Area

Hiking
Trail

Tents Only

4. Tents and campers are in the same area.   yes   no

5. The picnic area is near the tree fort.   yes   no

6. A bath house is by the lake.   yes   no

Reading Maps

Look at the map and the map key.
Then follow the directions.

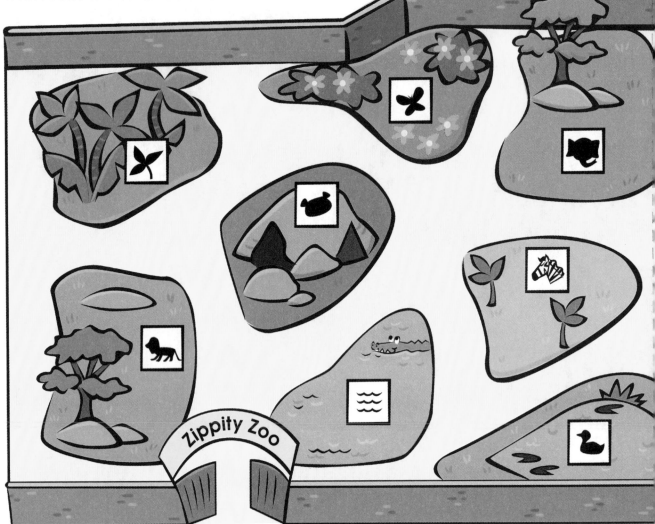

1. Draw a line to show a way to the snake house.

2. Draw a ☐ to show where you can see a tiger.

3. Draw a △ to show where you can see a duck.

4. Write the name of the place you would go first.

_____

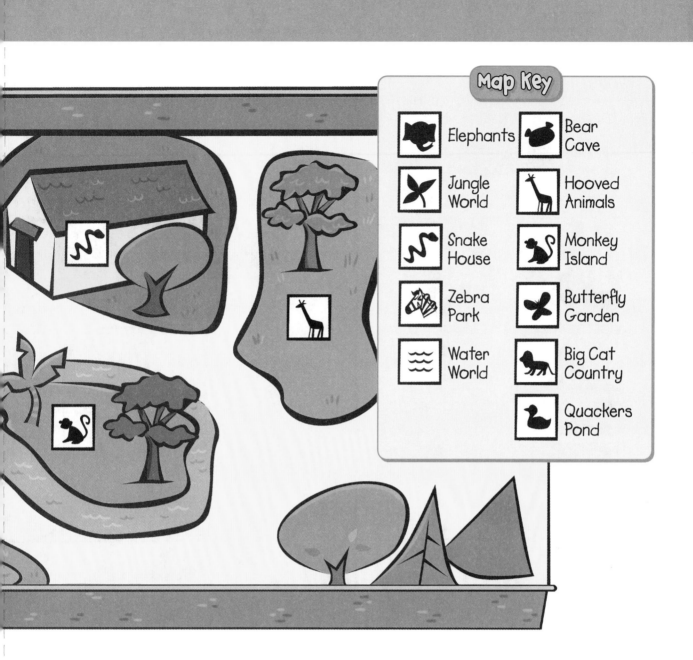

Map Key

	Elephants		Bear Cave
	Jungle World		Hooved Animals
	Snake House		Monkey Island
	Zebra Park		Butterfly Garden
	Water World		Big Cat Country
			Quackers Pond

Use the map to answer the questions.

5. Can you see an elephant in the zoo?   yes   no

6. Can you see a snake in the zoo?   yes   no

7. Can you see a snowman in the zoo?   yes   no

Reading Maps

OFF TO THE DUDE RANCH

Ethan and Avery went to Circle S Ranch for the summer.
They need help getting from the entrance to the riding stables.
Use the map to answer the questions.

Map Key

pueblo   ponderosa pine

ghost town   coyote

ranch house   blacksmith

stable   barbecue pit

pond   cactus

S Ranch

1. What will they pass first?   ghost town   cows

2. Will they turn at the ranch house?   yes   no

3. Will they cross over a bridge?   yes   no

4. What will they pass after the bridge?   coyote   pueblo

5. What is the last thing they will pass? barbecue pit   pond

6. Draw a line to show the path they followed.

Reading Maps   ©School Zone Publishing Company

7. Which two things would you like to see at Circle S Ranch?

_____

_____

_____

_____

_____

Reading Maps

Wendy and her mother are going shopping at the mall.
Use your pencil to follow their route.

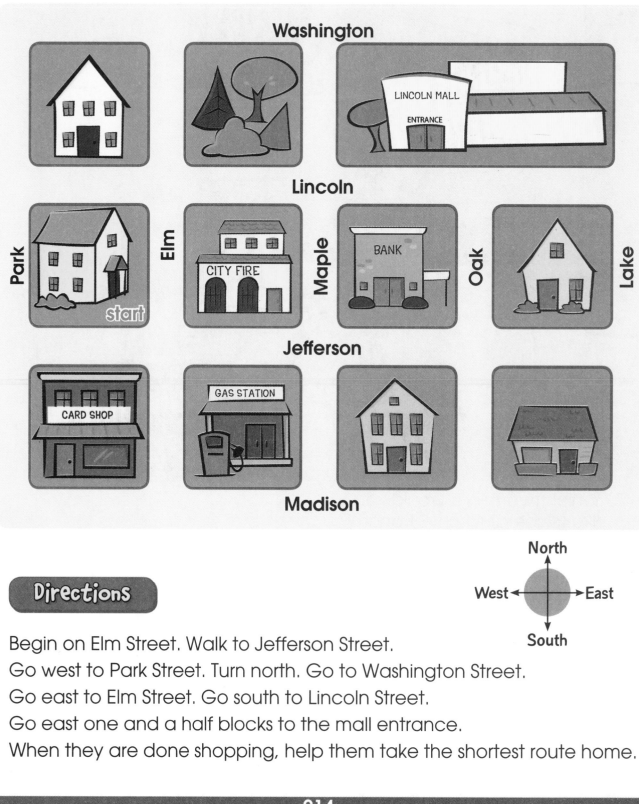

Directions

Begin on Elm Street. Walk to Jefferson Street.
Go west to Park Street. Turn north. Go to Washington Street.
Go east to Elm Street. Go south to Lincoln Street.
Go east one and a half blocks to the mall entrance.
When they are done shopping, help them take the shortest route home.

Reading Maps/Following Directions

©School Zone Publishing Company

Use the map to answer the questions.

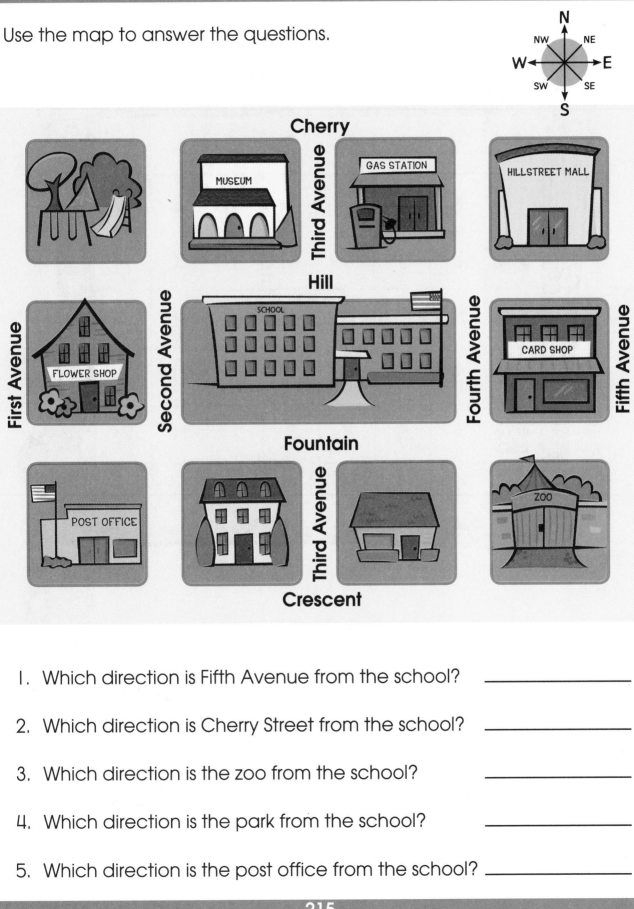

1. Which direction is Fifth Avenue from the school? _____

2. Which direction is Cherry Street from the school? _____

3. Which direction is the zoo from the school? _____

4. Which direction is the park from the school? _____

5. Which direction is the post office from the school? _____

Reading Maps

Use the code to solve the riddle.

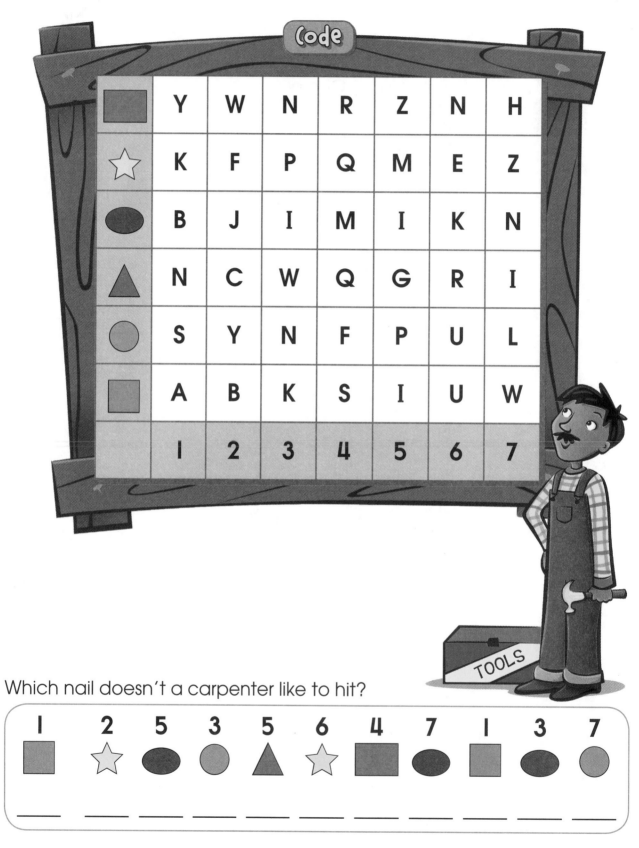

Code

	1	2	3	4	5	6	7
■	Y	W	N	R	Z	N	H
★	K	F	P	Q	M	E	Z
⬭	B	J	I	M	I	K	N
▲	N	C	W	Q	G	R	I
●	S	Y	N	F	P	U	L
◻	A	B	K	S	I	U	W

TOOLS

Which nail doesn't a carpenter like to hit?

1 2 5 3 5 6 4 7 1 3 7

_A_ _F_ _I_ _N_ _G_ _E_ _R_ _N_ _A_ _I_ _L_

Use the code to solve the riddle.

Code

	1	2	3	4	5	6	7
■	Y	U	R	N	N	E	I
☆	M	J	B	Z	J	A	P
⬭	G	L	L	T	Q	C	B
△	B	A	H	P	K	I	K
●	S	G	S	S	D	O	R
■	Q	L	B	D	V	N	U

Which kind of insect sleeps the most?

2	3	6	5	7	2	1
△	■	■	●	⬭	■	⬭

_____ _____ _____ _____ _____ _____ _____

217

Decoding Puzzle

NOUNS

Nouns are people, places, or things.

We are going to visit my <u>aunt</u>. (person)
She lives in a <u>forest</u>. (place)
She has a <u>puppy</u>. (animal)
She wrote a <u>book</u>. (thing)

Read the sentences.
Write the nouns that name people or animals.

1. Billy wanted to go. _____

2. Dad drove away. _____

3. The farmer waved. _____

4. The cows were eating. _____

5. Our dog barked. _____

6. A chicken ran away. _____

Write the correct nouns that name animals to finish the sentences.

pig horse dog duck cow goat

1. The _____ is tall.

2. A _____ has a curly tail.

3. The _____ is eating.

4. A spotted _____ moos.

5. The _____ has a green head.

6. The _____ has a purple collar.

Nouns/Picture Clues

Which words name places and which name things?
Write the nouns in the correct columns.

zoo   house   pizza   book   town   bike

places	things
_____	_____
_____	_____
_____	_____

Extra Credit!

Write a word that names a place and a word that names a thing.

place	thing
_____	_____

NOUNS

Nouns are words that name people, animals, places, or things.
Draw lines through the nouns.

People

1

and	pat	red
dad	mom	brother
blue	the	sing

Animals

2

did	eat	cat
bake	rabbit	do
dog	come	sit

Places

3

sad	big	school
small	hot	zoo
happy	cold	beach

Things

4

ball	talk	jump
run	bike	tall
wide	sheep	car

221

Read the story.
Underline the nouns.

My family is busy working on the farm.
The cows are being milked.
Hens are laying eggs.
A neighbor is painting the fence.
The horse waits in the barn.
My uncle is out in the field on his tractor.
My brother is feeding the chickens.

Write the nouns from the story in the correct columns.

people

_____

_____

_____

_____

animals

_____

_____

_____

_____

places

_____

_____

_____

things

_____

_____

_____

Nouns/Classifying

Many nouns add **s** to name more than one.

one hen → two hen**s**
one frog → two frog**s**

dog spot ball bone ear name

Finish the sentences by writing the correct nouns from the box, adding **s** to make the nouns plural.

1. Jamie has two _____.

2. Their _____ are Mia and Jet.

3. One dog has black ears and _____.

4. One dog has brown _____.

5. They run after _____.

6. They bury _____.

Plural nouns/Picture Clues

Proper nouns name particular people, animals, places, and things. All proper nouns begin with capital letters.

Name: Ben
Place: Yellowstone National Park
Thing: Hurricane George

Find the pets' names in the word search. Then answer the clues with proper nouns.

A	P	E	T	E	R	H	J
F	D	A	X	Z	T	S	P
Q	V	V	G	H	P	L	O
B	U	B	B	L	E	S	L
H	F	X	Y	U	H	V	L
D	U	K	E	W	J	N	Y
Z	S	Q	V	T	D	U	Q
D	P	U	F	F	M	K	L

Polly

Puff

Peter

Bubbles

Duke

1. I can talk. _____

2. I chase mice. _____

3. I hop. _____

4. I live in water. _____

5. I bark at strangers. _____

PROPER NOUNS

The days of the week, months of the year, and holidays are proper nouns.

Monday   September   Christmas

Sunday	Monday	Tuesday	Wednesday	Thursday	Friday	Saturday
Sherman Sheep Shearing	Birthday Party for Coco the Camel	Storytime Safari with Keeper Katie	The Zoo Is for You Day! FREE DAY	Jungle Day Walk with Monte Monkey	Dusty Desert Trail Hike	Spring Egg Hunt

Write the days when these things happen.

1. _____   2. _____

3. _____   4. _____

Proper Nouns/Reading Calendars

PROPER NOUNS

Read the town's special events calendar.

Sunday	Monday	Tuesday	Wednesday	Thursday	Friday	Saturday
Berry picking at Eno Farm	Farmer's Market opens today!	Berry Baking Contest	4th of July Parade 11:00	County Fair today through Saturday	Fireworks at the Lake 9:00	Blue Ribbon Day at the Fair

Write the days when these things happen.

1. _____

2. _____

3. _____

4. _____

Proper Nouns/Reading Calendars   ©School Zone Publishing Company

A **verb** is an action word that tells what someone or something does.

run   jump   laugh   cry   eat   sleep

Read the sentences.
Write the verbs.

1. Let's play ball. _____

2. Jake hits the ball. _____

3. The ball flies high. _____

4. Wen runs after it. _____

5. Will she catch it? _____

6. Will Wen drop the ball? _____

Verbs

VERBS

Roxanne wants to go to Suzie's house.
Help her get there by following the path of verbs.

Fun Fact

A verb doesn't always describe movement. For instance, sleep, rest, and think are verbs.

eat	run	dog	cat	big	rabbit
slide					bed
desk	jump	walk	small		sock
yarn		fly			bird
shell	house	dig	ball		shoes
city		hop			
car		climb			
cookie	wagon	hug	sing		

Some **verbs** end with **s**.

dig**s**   sing**s**   jump**s**

plant eat water pull dig grow

Finish the sentences by writing the correct verbs from the box, adding **s** as needed.

1. Each spring, Bob _____ a garden.

2. He _____ pretty flowers.

3. Dad _____ weeds.

4. Anna _____ the garden.

5. Sometimes, a rabbit _____ the flowers.

6. Sometimes, a dog _____ in the garden.

Adding "s" to Verbs

Read the story.
Underline the verbs.

Five ducks waddle to the pond.
They jump into the cool water.
They paddle with their feet.
They dive under the water.
They bob back up.
They swim to the other side.
Then they fly away.

Circle the verbs that tell what the ducks did.

1.	How do the ducks get to the pond?	walk	waddle
2.	How do they get into the cool water?	jump	hop
3.	How do they get to the other side?	slide	swim
4.	How do they leave?	fly	jog

Read the poem.
Underline the verbs.

She dashes and darts,
Scrambles and slides,
Bumps into walls,
Rolls on her sides,
Pounces on balls,
Leaps on the chair,
Spins round and round,
Pops up on the chair.
Then she sits.

1. Write a sentence using the verb "slides".

_____

_____

2. Write a sentence using the verb "flops".

_____

_____

NOUNS AND VERBS

Color the nouns **red**.
Color the verbs **green**.

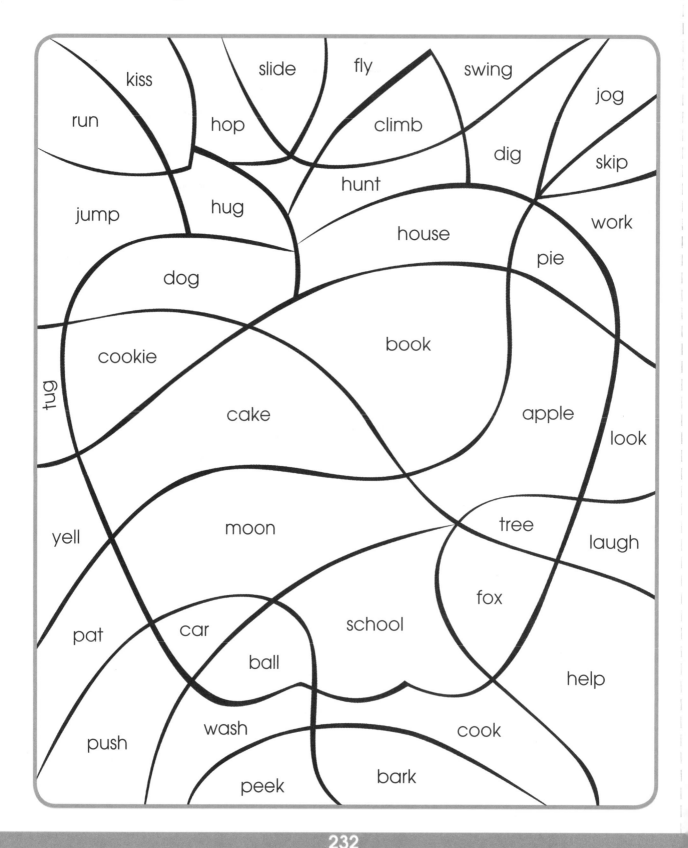

kiss
slide
fly
swing
run
hop
climb
jog
dig
skip
hunt
jump
hug
house
work
pie
dog
cookie
book
tug
cake
apple
look
yell
moon
tree
laugh
fox
pat
car
school
ball
help
push
wash
cook
peek
bark

An **adjective** is a describing word. It tells about a noun.
An adjective can be a number, size, or color.
An adjective can tell how something looks, sounds or feels.
Many adjectives come before the nouns they describe.

There are many ladybugs in the garden. "Many" is an adjective.

Read the story.
Underline the adjectives.

A ladybug is a small beetle.
It has a round body.
It may have red or orange wings.
The wings have black spots.
This tiny insect helps people.
Ladybugs eat harmful insects.

Circle the nouns that the adjectives describe.

1. "Small" describes		wings	beetle
2. "Red or orange" describes		wings	body
3. "Round" describes		body	spots
4. "Harmful" describes		wings	insects

Adjectives

Write the adjectives that fit the shapes.

sour soft cold hard sweet hot

1.

2.

3.

4.

5.

6.

7. Write two words from the box that tell how things taste.

_____   _____

Write the adjectives that describe the animals.

long tall tiny wet sleepy huge

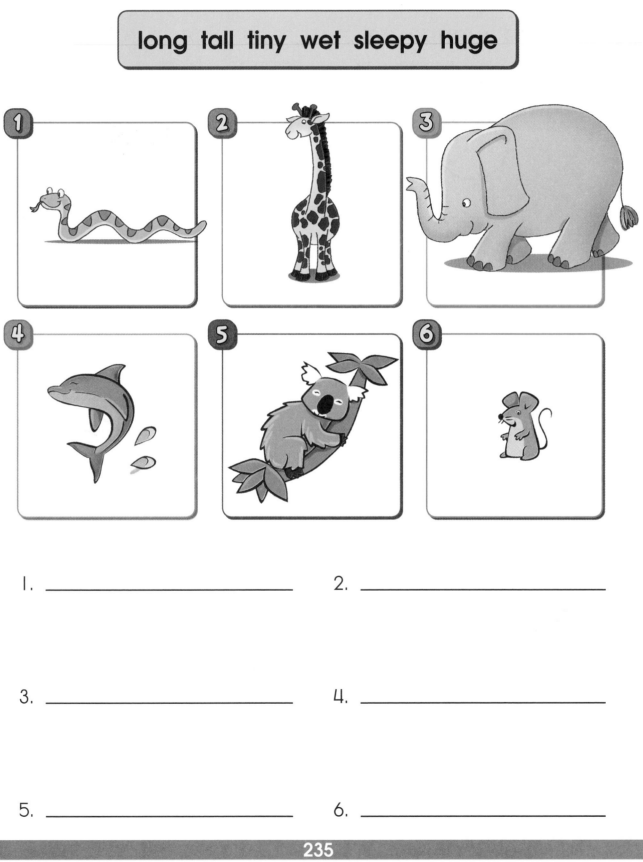

I. _____

2. _____

3. _____

4. _____

5. _____

6. _____

Adjectives

Write the adjectives that fit the shapes. Color the pieces of fruit.

red orange yellow green blue purple

1.

2.

3.

4.

5.

6.

Write the correct adjectives to finish the sentences.

hot cold loud wet quiet soft

1. The sun is _____.

2. A jet makes a _____ sound.

3. Ice cream is _____.

4. The kitten has _____ fur.

5. Don't slip on the _____ grass.

6. The _____ deer hides.

Adjectives

ADJECTIVES

Write the correct adjectives to finish the sentences.

1. I like to read on _____ days.

2. Kites fly high when it is _____ .

3. Days the sun is hidden are _____ .

4. We need to wear boots when it is _____ .

Adjectives

Color the adjectives that describe the weather yellow.
Color the other adjectives blue.

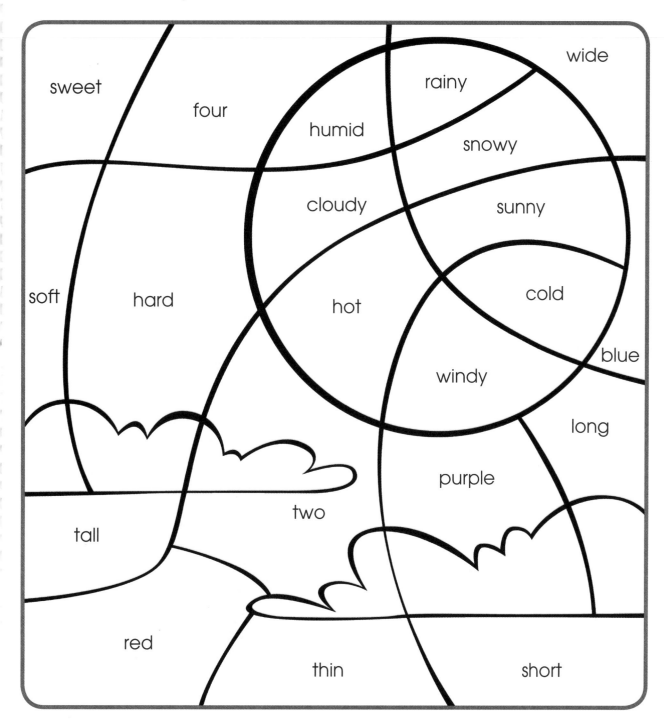

This is a picture of the _____ .

Read the sentences.
Underline the adjectives.
Draw lines from the sentences to the cats they describe.

1. Lady is a big cat.

2. She had three kittens.

3. Tiger is the striped kitten.

4. Jet is the black kitten.

5. The little kitten is Socks.

6. We now have four cats.

ADJECTIVES

Read the story.
Underline the adjectives.

There are many kinds of dogs.
Some dogs are very big.
Toy dogs are very small.
There are dogs with long hair.
Other dogs have short hair.
Some dogs help people hunt.
Some dogs help people work.
Dogs are good family pets.

Circle the correct answers.

1. How many kinds of dogs are there?   many   few   small

2. What kind of family pet does a dog make?   bad   fine   good

3. Which adjective is the opposite of "big"?   many   long   small

4. Which adjective is the opposite of "short"?   small   long   few

---

Extra Credit!

Write about a dog you would like to have.
Use adjectives such as its color and size.

_____

_____

_____

Adjectives

Read the story.
Circle the nouns.
Underline the verbs.
Draw a box around the adjectives.

Paul took his small dog for a long walk.
Paul saw a small fawn.
Then Paul saw a spotted frog sitting on a large log.
A black hawk made a loud "caw" sound as it flew by.
All in all, Paul and his dog had a fine walk that early dawn.

Circle the correct answers.

1. Which animal made a "caw" sound?
   fawn   frog   hawk

2. What kind of frog was sitting on the log?
   large   spotted   striped

3. When is dawn?
   morning   night   noon

4. What size was the dog?
   big   medium   small

The **subject** of a sentence tells who or what the sentence is about.

<u>My family</u> went on a trip.
"My family" tells who this sentence is about.

<u>The trip</u> took six hours.
"The trip" tells what this sentence is about.

Read the sentences.
Underline the subjects.
Then circle who or what.

1. Our family visited Yellowstone National Park.   who   what

2. The park has lakes and springs.   who   what

3. People camp in the park.   who   what

4. Stars fill the night sky.   who   what

5. Forests are everywhere.   who   what

6. Hikers climb hills.   who   what

Write subjects to finish the sentences.

7. _____ is fun to visit.

8. _____ and I go there a lot.

Sentence Parts: Subjects

In addition to a subject, a sentence also has a **predicate**.
The predicate includes a verb and tells what the subject is or does.

The friends <u>made plans for a picnic</u>.
"Made plans for a picnic" tells what "the friends" did.

Read the sentences.
Underline the predicates.

1. Dani brings milk.

2. Josh grabs bananas.

3. Kim takes a salad.

4. Billy carries hot dogs.

5. They all eat together.

Extra Credit!

Write a sentence about a picnic.
Underline the predicate.

Read the sentences.
Underline the predicates.

1. Owls hunt at night.

2. Elk eat green plants.

3. Eagles nest in the park.

4. Water shoots up from underground.

5. Hikers walk down trails.

6. The forest is quiet.

Write predicates to finish the sentences.

7. Campers _____ .

8. A squirrel _____ .

Sentence Parts: Predicates

Sometimes the **context**, or surrounding word clues, will help you understand a word you don't know. Practice using context clues to determine which word is missing.

The cheese was (moldy/tasty), so I threw it in the garbage.
You would throw moldy cheese in the garbage.

Circle the words that belong.
Underline the clues that helped you decide.

1. I love fruit, so I packed a
   (banana/pizza) for lunch.

2. A feather tickled my nose, so
   I (sneezed/cried).

3. The snow was (pretty/heavy).
   It broke the tree limb.

4. It was my birthday, so we had
   a (circus/party).

5. He gave his mom a rose.
   She (smiled/frowned) and said, "Thank you."

Context Clues/Correlation

Write the correct words to answer the riddles.

| when why which who where |

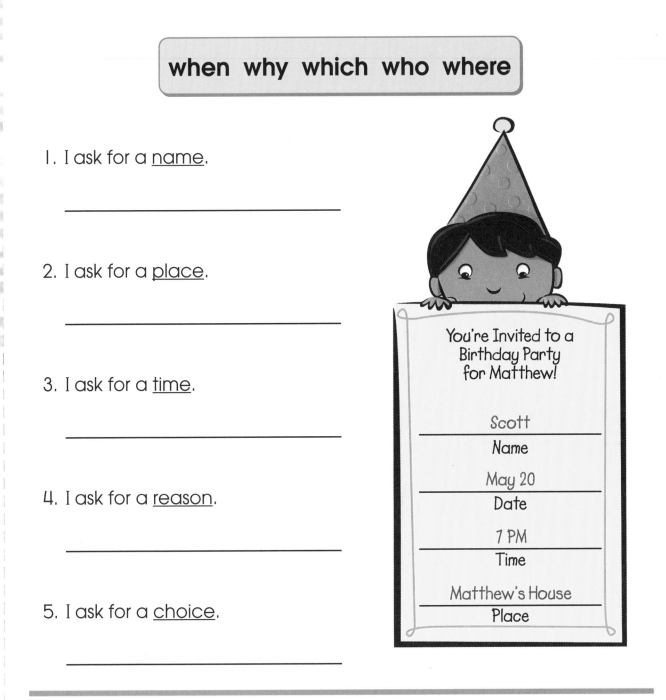

1. I ask for a <u>name</u>.

   _____

2. I ask for a <u>place</u>.

   _____

3. I ask for a <u>time</u>.

   _____

4. I ask for a <u>reason</u>.

   _____

5. I ask for a <u>choice</u>.

   _____

You're Invited to a
Birthday Party
for Matthew!

Scott
_____
Name

May 20
_____
Date

7 PM
_____
Time

Matthew's House
_____
Place

Extra Credit!

Write a sentence that asks <u>what</u>.

_____

Interrogative Words

WHO, WHAT, WHERE, WHEN, WHY, AND HOW?

Asking the questions "who", "what", "where", "when", "why", and "how" can help you understand a story.

Read the story below.
Answer the questions.

Tomorrow is Katie's birthday party. She is excited. Katie and her friend Lauren are going to ride the bus to the zoo. Katie wants to see the monkeys first because they are her favorite. After the zoo, Katie will have a pizza party at home and open her presents. It will be so much fun. She can't wait.

1. Who is having a birthday party?

_____

2. What will Katie do after the zoo?

_____

3. When is Katie's party?

_____

Interrogative Words   ©School Zone Publishing Company

4. Where is Katie's party?

_____

5. Why does Katie want to see the monkeys first?

_____

6. How will Katie and Lauren get to the zoo?

_____

7. What is the best title for this story? Circle it.

Katie's Pizza Party

Monkeys and Pizza

Katie's Exciting Birthday Party

Extra Credit!

Create your own title for this story.

_____

Interrogative Words

Follow the directions.
Then read the message that is left.

Color the **J** boxes red.
Color the **Q** boxes blue.
Color the **X** boxes green.
Color the **Z** boxes yellow.

J	Q	H	O	W	Z	M	A	N	Y
Z	X	I	N	C	H	E	S	Q	J
X	A	R	E	Z	X	I	N	J	X
Q	Z	A	J	Q	F	O	O	T	?

Write the hidden message. Then answer the question.

_____

_____

Follow the directions.
Then read the message that is left.

Color the **B** boxes **red**.
Color the **Q** boxes **blue**.
Color the **K** boxes **green**.
Color the **Z** boxes **yellow**.

K	H	O	W	Z	B	M	A	N	Y
Q	Z	M	O	N	T	H	S	K	B
A	R	E	Z	Q	B	K	I	N	Q
Q	B	A	K	Z	Y	E	A	R	?

Write the hidden message. Then answer the question.

_____

_____

Decoding Puzzle

An **analogy** is a comparison of similar things.
<u>Smile</u> is to <u>laugh</u> as <u>frown</u> is to <u>cry</u>.

Complete the analogies using words from the box.

king legs boil pound lie past

1. Chair is to sit as bed is to _____.

2. Princess is to prince as queen is to _____.

3. Today is to present as yesterday is to _____.

4. Freeze is to cold as _____ is to hot.

5. Scissors are to cut as hammer is to _____.

6. Wings are to birds as _____ are to people.

Extra Credit!

Write your own analogy.

_____

_____

Complete the analogies using words from the box.

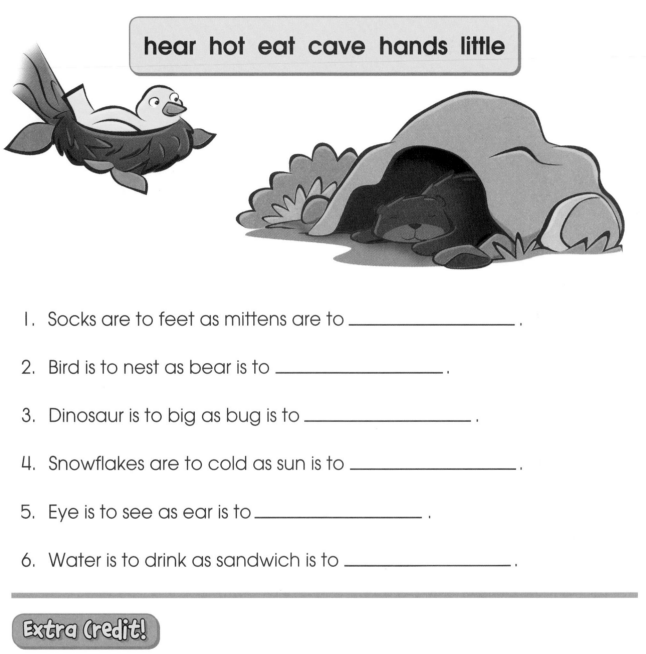

hear   hot   eat   cave   hands   little

1. Socks are to feet as mittens are to _____ .

2. Bird is to nest as bear is to _____ .

3. Dinosaur is to big as bug is to _____ .

4. Snowflakes are to cold as sun is to _____ .

5. Eye is to see as ear is to _____ .

6. Water is to drink as sandwich is to _____ .

Extra Credit!

Write your own analogy.

_____

_____

_____

Analogies

Complete the analogies using words from the box.

| sky sheep wild weight work happy |

1. Car is to road as plane is to _____.

2. Clock is to time as scale is to _____.

3. Milk is to cow as wool is to _____.

4. Dog is to tame as tiger is to _____.

5. Cry is to sad as laugh is to _____.

6. School is to learn as job is to _____.

Extra Credit!

Write your own analogy.

_____

_____

_____

SOUNDS FISHY

Why are fish so smart?
Follow the directions.
Then read the message that is left.

Color the **K** boxes green.
Color the **V** boxes red.
Color the **X** boxes blue.
Color the **P** boxes orange.

X	V	T	H	E	Y	P	G	O	V	P
V	P	X	K	V	P	X	V	P	K	x
P	X	A	R	O	U	N	D	V	X	P
K	V	K	X	V	V	K	X	P	V	K
I	N	P	S	C	H	O	O	L	S	.

Write the answer to the riddle.

_____

_____

©School Zone Publishing Company

Decoding Puzzle

HIDDEN MESSAGE

Follow the directions.
Then read the message that is left.

Color the **Y** boxes **red**.
Color the **C** boxes **blue**.
Color the **J** boxes **orange**.
Color the **H** boxes **green**.
Color the **Z** boxes **purple**.

Y	I	C	J	Z	L	I	K	E	C	J
R	E	D	C	J	Z	Y	H	J	Y	C
H	Z	Y	F	L	O	W	E	R	S	H
A	N	D	Y	P	U	R	P	L	E	Z
C	J	B	A	L	L	O	O	N	S	.

Write the hidden message.

_____

_____

256

Decoding Puzzle   ©School Zone Publishing Company

STATEMENTS

A **statement** is a sentence that tells something.
A statement begins with a capital letter and ends with a **period** (.).

Our dog's name is Skip.

Use ☰ to show where capital letters go.
Put periods (.) at the end of the sentences.
The first one is done for you.

1. <u>our</u> dog is hungry.

2. dad brings food

3. skip eats quickly

4. food goes on the floor

5. dogs are messy

6. now I need to clean up

Extra Credit!

Write a statement.

_____

_____

Types of Sentences: Statements

A **question** is a sentence that asks about someone or something.
A question begins with a capital letter and ends with a **question mark** (?).

What is your favorite color?

Use ☰ to show where capital letters go.
Put question marks at the end of the sentences that ask questions.
Put a period at the end of the telling sentence.
The first one is done for you.

1. i̲s Mother home?

2. where did she go

3. when will she be back

4. who baked the cookies

5. they are good

6. may i have another one

Extra Credit!

Write a question.

_____

_____

An **exclamation** is a sentence that shows strong feeling.
An exclamation begins with a capital letter and ends
with an **exclamation point** (!).

I can't believe we won!
We're the best!

Write exclamation points at the end of the exclamations.
Write periods at the end of the statements.

1. My team played soccer today

2. The most amazing thing happened

3. The score was 3 to 3

4. Our team got the ball

5. We made a goal

6. It was awesome

Extra Credit!

Write an exclamation.

_____

_____

Types of Sentences: Exclamations

Use the code to solve the riddle.

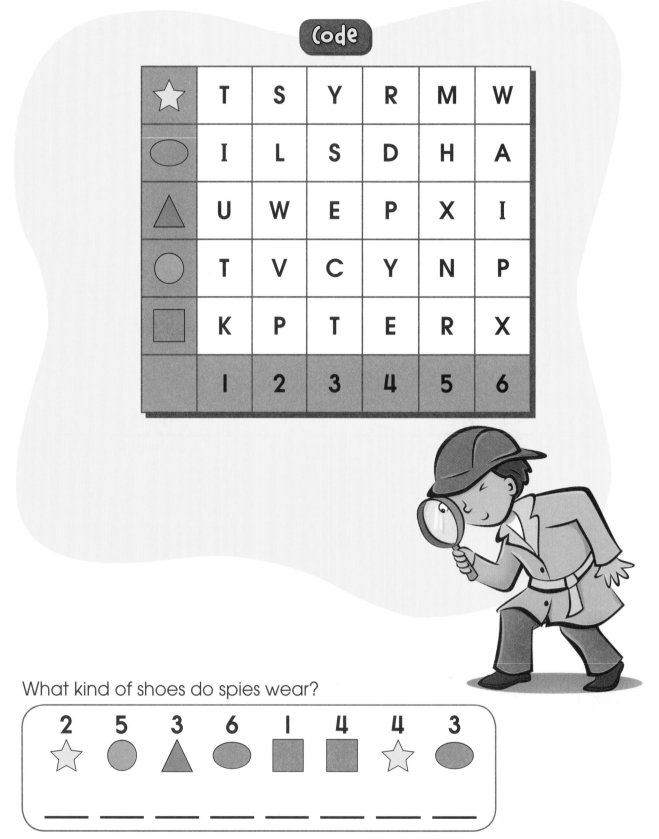

Code

	1	2	3	4	5	6
★	T	S	Y	R	M	W
⬭	I	L	S	D	H	A
△	U	W	E	P	X	I
○	T	V	C	Y	N	P
◻	K	P	T	E	R	X

What kind of shoes do spies wear?

2	5	3	6	1	4	4	3
★	○	△	⬭	◻	◻	★	⬭

___ ___ ___ ___ ___ ___ ___ ___

Decoding Puzzle ©School Zone Publishing Company

Write the names of the colors in their numbered rows in the puzzle.
Use the code to answer the question.

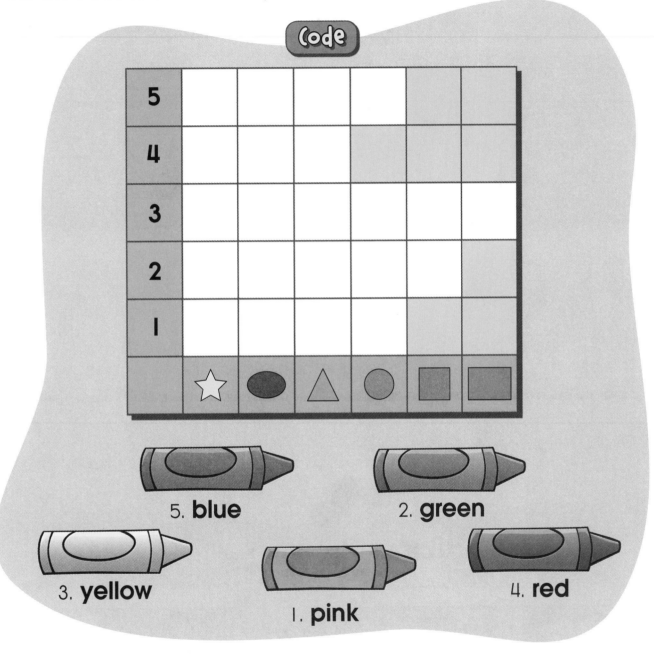

5. **blue**

2. **green**

3. **yellow**

1. **pink**

4. **red**

What color do you get when you mix red and blue?

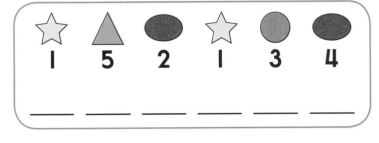

| 1 | 5 | 2 | 1 | 3 | 4 |

___ ___ ___ ___ ___ ___

Decoding Puzzle

The snowman is melting.

Why did this happen?

The sun came out and the temperature rose.

The sun and the rising temperature **caused** the snowman to melt.
The **effect** of the sun and the rising temperature is the melting snowman.

Read the effect. Write the cause.

The dog is eating.

Why did this happen?

_____

_____

Read the effects. Write the causes.

1. The sidewalk has dog prints in it.

Why did this happen?

_____

_____

2. A dog has a ball in his mouth.

Why did this happen?

_____

_____

Cause and Effect Relationships

CAUSE AND EFFECT RELATIONSHIPS

Read the effects. Write the causes.

1. Jason has a tomato from the garden.

Why did this happen?

_____

_____

2. The bird feeder is filling up with birdseed.

Why did this happen?

_____

_____

CAUSE AND EFFECT RELATIONSHIPS

Put check marks by what you think will happen next.

1. The baby is hungry.

   _____ The baby is given a toy.

   _____ The baby is given dinner.

2. The family dog is lost.

   _____ The family looks for it.

   _____ The family watches TV.

3. It begins to rain at the picnic.

   _____ The family eats.

   _____ The family packs up and leaves.

4. The car has a flat tire.

   _____ The tire is fixed.

   _____ The car is sold.

5. Bill's shirt is torn.

   _____ Bill wears the torn shirt.

   _____ Bill puts on a new shirt.

Cause and Effect Relationships

Circle the pictures that show what happened next.

1. Mick loves movies. He goes to a movie whenever he has money. Mick got $10.00 from his uncle. What happened next?

2. Morgan's mom gave her flower seeds. Morgan made a garden. She planted the seeds every which way. What happened next?

3. Mia's pup chewed her homework. He chewed a chair leg. Mia left her shoes in the yard. What happened next?

CAUSE AND EFFECT RELATIONSHIPS

Circle the pictures that show what happened next.

1. Jack turned on the water. He was going to wash the dishes. Jack started talking to his friend. What happened next?

2. Kathy's mom went out. Kathy cleaned the house. Her mom came home. What happened next?

3. Eva went to the library. She picked out a book. She couldn't wait to read it. Eva took the book home. What happened next?

Cause and Effect Relationships

Draw lines from the causes to the effects.

Cause   **Effect**

Write about the cause and effects.

1. What would happen if you dropped a glass?

_____

2. What would happen if you touched something hot?

_____

3. What would cause you to laugh?

_____

Look at the pictures.
Write the names of the pictures in their numbered rows in the puzzle.
Use the code to solve the riddle.

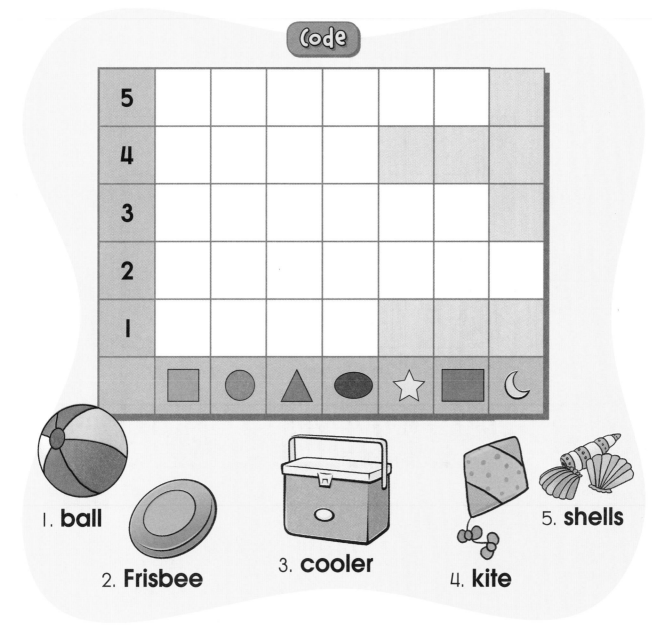

Code

1. ball

2. Frisbee

3. cooler

4. kite

5. shells

Where do you go on a hot summer day?

4 5 2   2 4 1 3 5

_____ _____ _____   _____ _____ _____ _____ _____

Decoding Puzzle

Use the code to solve the riddle.

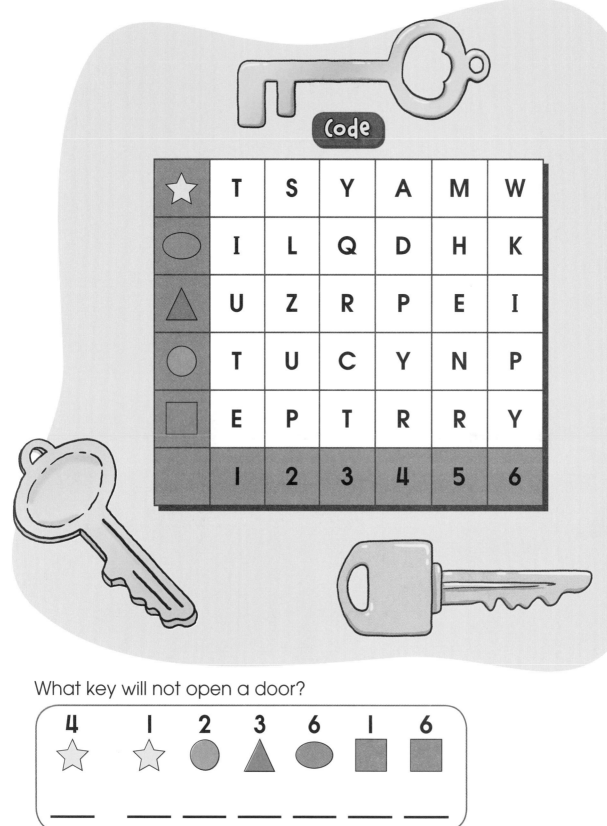

Code

	1	2	3	4	5	6
★	T	S	Y	A	M	W
⬭	I	L	Q	D	H	K
△	U	Z	R	P	E	I
◯	T	U	C	Y	N	P
▢	E	P	T	R	R	Y
	1	2	3	4	5	6

What key will not open a door?

4	1	2	3	6	1	6
★	★	◯	△	⬭	▢	▢

___ ___ ___ ___ ___ ___ ___

Read the story.

This is my cat.
His name is Pat.
Pat sat on his mat.
Oh! Pat saw a bat.
Pat ran after the bat.
Drat!
Pat could not catch the bat.
Pat sat back on his mat.

Number the sentences from
1 to 4 to show the correct order.

_____ Pat ran after the bat.

_____ Pat could not catch the bat.

_____ Pat sat back on his mat.

_____ Pat saw a bat.

Story Order

SID THE SNAKE

Read the story.

Sid the Snake makes shapes.
Sid can make a circle.
Sid can make an s.
Sid cannot make a triangle.
Sid cannot make a square.

Circle the correct answers.

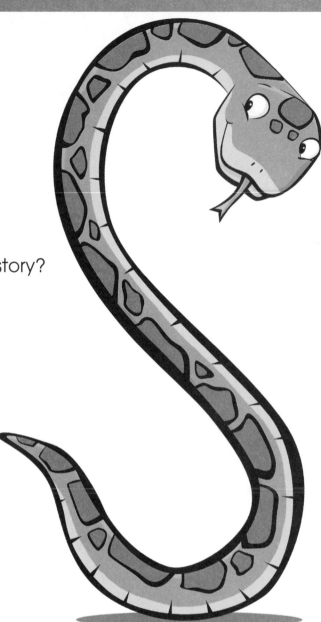

1. What is the best name for the story?

   Real Snake   Sid's Shapes

2. What shape can Sid make?

   circle   square

3. Can Sid make a triangle?

   yes   no

4. Can Sid make an s?

   yes   no

5. Draw a square.

6. Draw a triangle.

Main Idea/Details

Read the story.

Amy got on the bus.
It was her first bus ride ever.
Amy sat next to her friend Sue.
The bus stopped many times.
Other kids got on the bus.

Circle the correct answers.

1. What did Amy get on?   bus   boat

2. Who did Amy sit next to?   Jon   Sue

3. Who else got on the bus?   dogs   kids

4. Had Amy been on a bus ride before?   yes   no

5. Did the bus stop a lot?   yes   no

6. Where was the bus going?   school   home

7. How many stops did the bus make?_____

273

Read the story.

Ben has a pet hen.
The hen is red.
The hen lives in a pen.
The red hen lays eggs for Ben.
She lays one egg a day.
How many days until Ben has ten? _____

Put check marks by the correct answers.

1. Which is the best title for the story?

   _____ Ben's Hen

   _____ Ben Likes Breakfast

   _____ The Hen's Pen

2. Which sentence tells what the story is about?

   _____ The hen lays eggs.

   _____ Ben has a pet hen.

   _____ The hen lives in a pen.

Main Idea/Details

Read the story.

Anna was in a bike race.
There were five riders in the race.
They lined up to begin.
Anna got a surprise.
Her bike had a flat tire!
Anna did not mind.
She will try another time.

1. Put a check mark by what the story is about.

   _____ Anna was in a bike race.

   _____ Her bike had a flat tire.

   _____ Anna did not mind.

   _____ Anna got a surprise.

2. Write how many riders were in the race? _____

Extra Credit!

Write a sentence about something that happened to you.

_____

_____

_____

Main Idea/Details

THE FOX ON THE ROCK

Read the story.

Scott was on the dock.
He had a fishing rod.
Scott saw something on the rock.
It was a fox.
The fox saw Scott.
It ran from the rock.
That is the last Scott saw of the fox.

Write T if the sentences are true.
Write F if the sentences are false.

1. _____ The fox was on the dock.

2. _____ Scott saw a fox.

3. _____ The fox ran from the rock.

4. _____ The fox had a fishing rod.

Extra Credit!

Write a sentence about what you would do if you saw a fox.

_____

_____

_____

_____

Read the story.

It was Play Day for the garden animals.
The turtle and snail decided to race.
First, they had to find a safe place.
They found a trail near the gate.
Wait! It is beginning to rain.
Waves of water washed out the trail.
The race never took place.

Answer the questions.

1. Who do you think would have won the race?

   _____

2. Which is the best title for the story?
   Put a check mark by your answer.

   _____The Trail

   _____Near the Gate

   _____Play Day

   _____Waves of Water

Extra Credit!

Write about the animals you would like to see race and why.

_____

_____

_____

Main Idea/Inference

Read the story.

Eric was walking to school.
There were puddles by the road.
A car went past.
Eric looked surprised.

Circle the correct answers.

1. What was Eric doing?

   walking to school

   walking to the park

2. Why did Eric look surprised?

   He did not know the driver.

   The car splashed water on him.

Extra Credit!

Write what you think Eric will do next.

_____

_____

_____

_____

Details/Making Inferences

LOST AND FOUND

Read the story.

Jill went shopping for shoes.
She lost her purse.
A call came from the lost-and-found desk.
Jill looked happy after the call.

Circle the correct answers.

1. What was Jill doing?

   shopping for shoes

   shopping for groceries

2. What did Jill lose?

   her hat

   her purse

3. Why do you think Jill looked happy?

   Her purse had been found.

   The store had the shoes she wanted.

Extra Credit!

Write what you think Jill will do next.

_____

_____

_____

THE BUG

Read the story.

Willie was a little car.
But everyone called him "The Bug".
He could not go fast,
But he was always ready.

One day, the family had a problem.
They got in their fast car.
It did not work,
But Willie was ready.
Willie saved the day!

Answer the questions.

1. What is the story about?

   _____

2. What was it that Willie could not do?

   _____

___

Extra Credit!

Write about a problem you have had.
How did you solve the problem?

_____

_____

_____

_____

ain Idea/Details   ©School Zone Publishing Company

Read the story.

Mouse needed a new house.
It did not have to be big.
It did not have to be pretty.
It had to be dry.
It had to be warm.
Winter was coming soon.

Mouse looked in a tree.
It was not warm.
Mouse looked under a leaf.
It was not dry.
Mouse found a boot.
Mouse had a new home!

Answer the questions.

1. What was the story about?

   _____

2. What did the house have to be?

   _____

3. Why did Mouse need a house?

   _____

Main Idea/Details

A SCARY NIGHTMARE

Read the story.

Henry was sleeping.
He dreamed he was being chased.
A lion wanted to eat him!
The lion was red.
Then it was blue.
Then it was yellow.
The jungle changed color also.
But the lion's teeth were always white.
Finally, Henry woke up.
He was glad the dream was over!

Circle the correct answers.

1. What did Henry dream about?

    a lion chasing him   rainbows in the sky

2. Where were Henry and the lion together?

    in the jungle   on a rainbow   at the park

3. What is a "nightmare"?

    a bad dream   a lion   teeth

Extra Credit!

Write about a bad dream you have had.

_____

_____

_____

Main Idea/Details   ©School Zone Publishing Company

GROWING, GROWING...

Read the story.

Josh grew a watermelon.
In the spring, he planted seeds.
He watered his plants each day.
The sun made the plants grow.
By the summer, one watermelon was huge!
He brought it to the fair.
He won a blue ribbon!

Circle the correct answers.

1. Who was the story about?

    Dani   Josh   Pedro

2. Which fruit was grown?

    apples   watermelon   bananas

3. What did the plants need?

    water, rain, clouds   soil, sun, plants   soil, water, sun

4. In which season was the fair?

    winter   spring   summer

Details

THE ROBIN

Read the story.

A robin made a nest in a tree.
She laid three eggs in the nest.
Then she sat on the eggs.
Fourteen days later, the eggs hatched.
The little chicks began to grow feathers.
The robin brought them worms and bugs to eat.
The chicks stayed in the nest 15 days after they hatched.
Then they were ready to leave the nest.

Answer the questions.

1. How long did it take for the eggs to hatch?

   _____

2. How many eggs were in the nest?

   _____

3. What did the chicks eat?

   _____

Details

Read the riddle.

You see me at the beach.
You see me in a game.
I am round and filled with air.
Sometimes, I can bounce.

Some people use me to float.
Some people use me to play catch.
Some people try to sit on me.
What am I?

Circle the correct answers.

1. What kind of writing is this?

   a note   a riddle   a sign

2. What is the riddle about?

   a swimsuit   a towel

   a beach ball   a float

3. Can it sometimes bounce?   yes   no

4. Is it always red?   yes   no

5. Is it round?   yes   no

6. Can it float?   yes   no

Genre/Inference/Details

Read the alphabet rhyme.

A-B-C-D and E-F-G
I knew that when I was three.

H-I-J-K and L-M-N-O-P
Q-R-S and T-U-V
Letters make the words I see.

W-X and Y and Z
The alphabet is fun for me!

Circle the correct answers.

1. What is the poem about?

    the sun   the alphabet

2. What is another good name for the poem?
    Letter Fun   Happy Birthday

3. What makes the words we see?
    letters   me

4. What is the alphabet for me?
    easy   fun

Read the poem.

Our team is the best.
Our team never rests.

Our team really hits.
Our team never quits.

Before the games begin,
We know that we will win!

Our team never rests.
Our team is the best!

Circle the correct answers.

1. What is the poem about?

   our family   our baseball team

   our school   our church

2. What is a team?

   a group working together to win

   a group working together to lose

3. What does our team never do?

   win   lose

   quit   hit

Main Idea/Details

Read the poem.

I can read a book.
I can learn to cook.
I can count to 103.

I can walk with a wiggle
That makes you giggle
Or buzz like a bumblebee.

It will always be true
That I am not just like you,
But I make a wonderful me!

Circle the correct answers.

1. What is the best name for the poem?

   I'm the Best Me!   I Am Better Than you

   I Can Buzz   I Am Pretty

2. Which word rhymes with "giggle"?
   make   wiggle   bumblebee

3. What does "wonderful" mean?
   bad   really great   silly

___

Extra Credit!

Write about something that makes you special.

_____

NIGHT POEM

Read the poem.

The moon tonight is full and bright.
The stars are shining high.

A falling star flies before my eyes.
I make a wish as it goes by.

The darkness creeps, but it's time to sleep.
I say "goodnight" to the sky.

Circle the correct answers.

1. What is not named in the poem?

   the stars   the sun   a falling star

2. Which word rhymes with "tonight"?

   high   sky   bright

3. What is full and bright?

   the moon   the stars   darkness

4. Which word means "move slowly".   creeps   bright

5. Which word means "goes through the air"?   sleep   flies

Main Idea/Details/Inference

JUMPING CHANT

Read the poem.

Flowers in the garden.
Flowers by the walk.
Flowers in the forest.
I wish that they could talk.

Flowers dancing in the wind
And sprouting up in May.
If I met a flower friend,
What would I have to say?

Circle the correct answers.

1. What kind of writing is this?
   a letter   a story   a poem

2. What do flowers do in the wind?
   grow   dance   talk

3. What does "sprouting up" mean?
   getting planted   starting to grow

Draw lines between the words that rhyme.

4. walk   shower

5. May   talk

6. flower   say

7. wish   fish

290

Read the note.

> Mom,
> I'm outside. I went to
> the park. Adam is with me.
> We will be home by noon.
>   I love you,
>   Erica

Answer the questions.

1. Who wrote the note?

   _____

2. Who is with Erica?

   _____

3. Where are they going?

   _____

4. When will they be home?

   _____

Details

Read the note.

Dear Jeremy,
We're having a party on the 4th of July. We can watch fireworks! Will you come? There will be a picnic at 6:00. Bring food you like to eat.
See you there,
Tyrone

Answer the questions.

1. What kind of writing is this?

   an invitation   a song   a book

2. What kind of party is it?

   _____

3. What time is the party?

   _____

4. What should Jeremy bring?

   _____

5. What will they do at the party?

   _____

Read the sign.

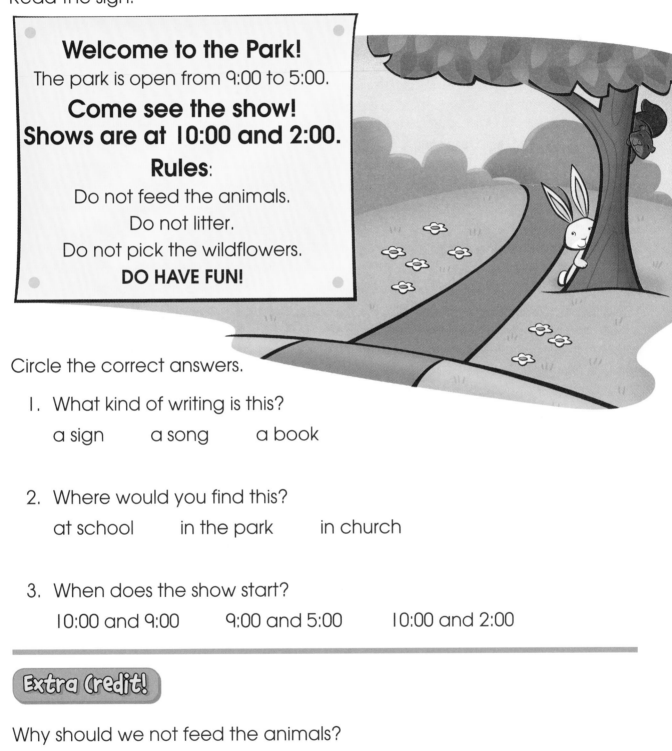

Welcome to the Park!
The park is open from 9:00 to 5:00.
Come see the show!
Shows are at 10:00 and 2:00.
Rules:
Do not feed the animals.
Do not litter.
Do not pick the wildflowers.
DO HAVE FUN!

Circle the correct answers.

1. What kind of writing is this?

   a sign   a song   a book

2. Where would you find this?

   at school   in the park   in church

3. When does the show start?

   10:00 and 9:00   9:00 and 5:00   10:00 and 2:00

Extra Credit!

Why should we not feed the animals?

_____

_____

Details/Inference

Read the postcards.
Write the correct names on the cards.
Use the numbered sentences for clues.

Howdy,

This ranch is lots of fun. I rode a horse named Sugarlump. I learned to rope a calf. There is a cookout tonight.

Love,

_____

Hi,

We are having a great time camping. We saw a deer and a bear yesterday. Wish you were here.

Hugs,

_____

Write words from the box to answer the questions.

deer ocean calf bear horse desert

1. Will and Abby saw what animals? _____

2. Where did Leah swim? _____

Hi,

The desert is neat. One cactus is taller than my house! I heard a coyote last night.
See you soon,

_____

Hi,

The ocean is great! I've swam every day. I have made three sandcastles. Wish you were here to look for seashells.

Sincerely,

_____

3. What animal did Pedro rope?_____

4. Who is Sugarlump?_____

5. Billy saw a cactus. Where does a cactus grow? _____

295

Details/Inference

Read the story.

Sshh... You are in a library.
People read in the library.
Please be quiet.

You can pick out a book at the library.
You can take the book home to read it.
Remember to bring the book back!

Circle the correct answers.

1. What is the story about?

   people   real things

   the library   storybooks

2. What can you do at the library?

   pick out a book   watch a show

   eat lunch   make noise

3. What should you remember to do with your book?

   be quiet   bring it back   give it away

4. Number the sentences from 1 to 3 to show the correct order.

   _____ Take the book home to read it.

   _____ Pick out a book.

   _____ Bring the book back to the library.

Read about book covers.

Books covers tell about books.
The words on the cover tell the
name of the book.
They tell who wrote the book.
They tell who drew the pictures.

Circle the correct answers.

1. Which things do book covers tell us?

who wrote the book   the name of the book

when the book was made   who drew the pictures

Read the book cover.
Then answer the questions.

2. Who wrote this book?

_____

3. Who drew the pictures inside this book?

_____

4. What do you think this book is about?

_____

Details

FRIENDS

Read about friends.

Friends are people who care about you.
They want you to be happy.
They like to be with you.

Friends are special people.
They share your feelings.
Friends make the world a better place.

Circle the correct answers.

1. What are two things friends do?

   They make the world bad.   They do not care.

   They share your feelings.   They want you to be happy.

Draw lines to put the sentences together.

2. Friends are people   to be happy.

3. They want you   special people.

4. They like to   who care about you.

5. Friends are   be with you.

6. Friends make the world   a better place.

Extra Credit!

Who is your friend?
What do you do together?

_____

_____

THE SUN

Read the facts about our Sun.

The Sun is a star.
Earth spins around it once a year.
The Sun is much larger than Earth.
The Sun gives us light.
It also give us heat.
There could be no life without the Sun.

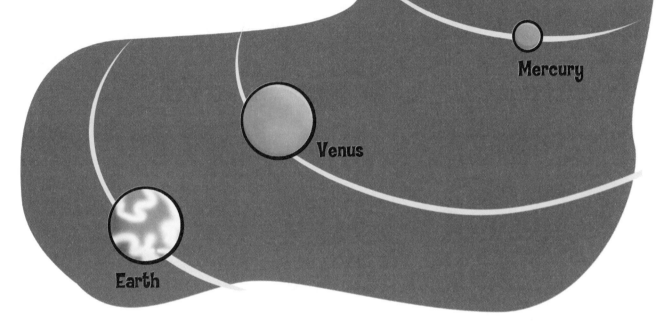

Circle the correct answers.

1. Once a year, Earth circles the Sun.   true   false

2. Earth give us light and heat.   true   false

3. The Sun is a star.   true   false

4. Earth is larger than the Sun.   true   false

5. There could be no life without the Sun.   true   false

Details

Read about the American flag.

This is our American flag.
Our flag is red, white, and blue.
Our flag has 13 stripes.
There are 7 red stripes.
There are 6 white stripes.
There are 50 stars.
There is one star for each state.

Circle the correct answers.

1. What is the story about?

    the flag   colors

    stars   stripes

2. How many stripes does the flag have?

    50 red, 13 white   7 red, 6 white

    6 red, 7 white   13 red, 50 white

3. Why are there 50 stars?

    There are 50 states.   The stars are small.

    There are 50 stripes.   There are 50 stars in the sky.

Extra Credit!

Design your own flag.

Read about birds.

Birds are the only animals with feathers.
A bird's longest feathers are the wing feathers and tail feathers.
Birds also have soft, downy feathers.
They fluff these feathers to help keep themselves warm.
At least once a year, birds shed their feathers and grow new ones.

Circle the correct answers.

1. What is the main idea of the story?

   downy feathers

   bird feathers

   flying birds

2. What happens to the feathers at least once a year?

   They change colors.

   They are washed.

   They are shed.

3. Which feathers do birds fluff to keep warm?

   tail feathers

   wing feathers

   downy feathers

Main Idea/Details

Read the story about bugs.

I do not think bugs are fun!
What can you do with a bug?
Can you give a bug a hug?
I go mad with their buzz, buzz, buzz.
When I see a bug, I want to run.
I do not think bugs are fun!

We sometimes call insects "bugs".

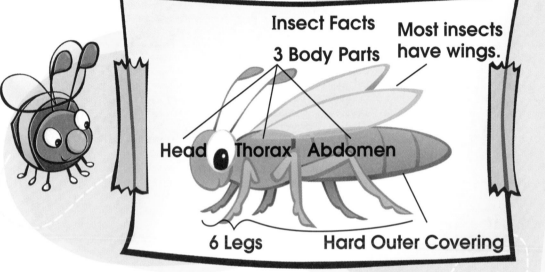

Insect Facts

3 Body Parts

Most insects have wings.

Head   Thorax   Abdomen

6 Legs   **Hard Outer Covering**

Write T if the sentences are true.
Write F if the sentences are false.

1. _____ Insects have six legs.

2. _____ Most insects have wings.

3. _____ An insect's body has three parts.

4. _____ Insects do not have a hard outer covering.

Read about snails.

A snail has a soft body covered by a shell.
It creeps along on a foot.
A snail makes a sticky slime to help it move.
Many land snails eat rotting plants.
They lay eggs in the ground.
Land snails live in shady places.

Answer the questions.

1. How do snails move?

_____

2. Where do land snails live?

_____

3. What do many land snails eat?

_____

4. Where do snails lay their eggs?

_____

Details

Read about frogs.

Frogs are plump, little animals with long back legs.
Their big eyes can see in all directions.
They flick out their sticky tongues to catch insects.
There are many kinds of frogs.
Frogs begin life in water.

Answer the questions.

1. What helps frogs catch insects?

    _____

2. What makes frog eyes special?

    _____

3. Where do frogs begin life?

    _____

Read about ducks.

A duck is a bird that lives near water.
There are many kinds of ducks.
Their webbed feet act as paddles to help them swim.
Ducks have oil on their feathers.
The oil makes the feathers waterproof.
Their feathers help keep ducks warm.

Answer the questions.

1. What helps ducks stay warm in the water?

   _____

2. Where do ducks live?

   _____

3. Why do the feet of ducks help them swim?

   _____

4. What is the best title for this story?
   Circle it.

   All about Ducks

   Ducklings

   Duck Eggs

©School Zone Publishing Company Main Idea/Details

Read about butterflies.

Butterflies are beautiful insects.
They are covered with thousands of tiny scales.
The scales are what give butterflies their colors.
Their colors help butterflies hide from danger.
Bright colors warn enemies that they taste bad.
Scales can also help control their temperature.
Butterflies live almost everywhere in the world.

Circle the correct answers.

1. What is a good title for the story?

   Butterfly Stories

   Millions of Scales

   Butterfly Wings

2. What are three ways that scales help butterflies?

   They help butterflies eat.

   They help butterflies escape harm.

   Scales help control their temperature.

   The bright colors warn away enemies.

DINOSAUR BONES

Read about dinosaur bones.

We know about dinosaurs from their bones.
People hunt for dinosaur bones all over the world.
They look in places where other bones were found.
Dinosaur bones can tell us how big dinosaurs were.
Bones can tell us what shape they were.
Bones cannot tell us what colors dinosaurs were.
Nobody knows for sure.

Circle the correct answers.

1. How do we know about dinosaurs?

    from their size   from their shape   from their bones

2. What do dinosaur bones tell us?

    what size they were   what colors they were   what they ate

3. What do the bones not tell us?

    their shape   their size   their colors

4. Where do people look for bones?

    in backyards   all over the world   in the sea

Extra Credit!

Write about where would you look for dinosaur bones.

_____

_____

Details

The **setting** is where a story takes place.
Characters are the actors in a story.

Read the story.

Carter woke up early.
He had a lot of chores to do.
First, he collected eggs from the chickens.
Next, he fed the cows and pigs.
Last, he brushed the horses.
When Carter finished, he helped his mom make breakfast.
After breakfast, he went outside and played.

Answer the questions.

1. Based on the clues, where does this story take place?

   _____

2. Underline the clues in the story that helped you figure out the setting.

3. Would you like to live where Carter does? Why or why not?

   _____

   _____

   _____

   _____

   _____

4. Who is the main character in this story?

_____

5. Cross out the words that do not describe Carter.

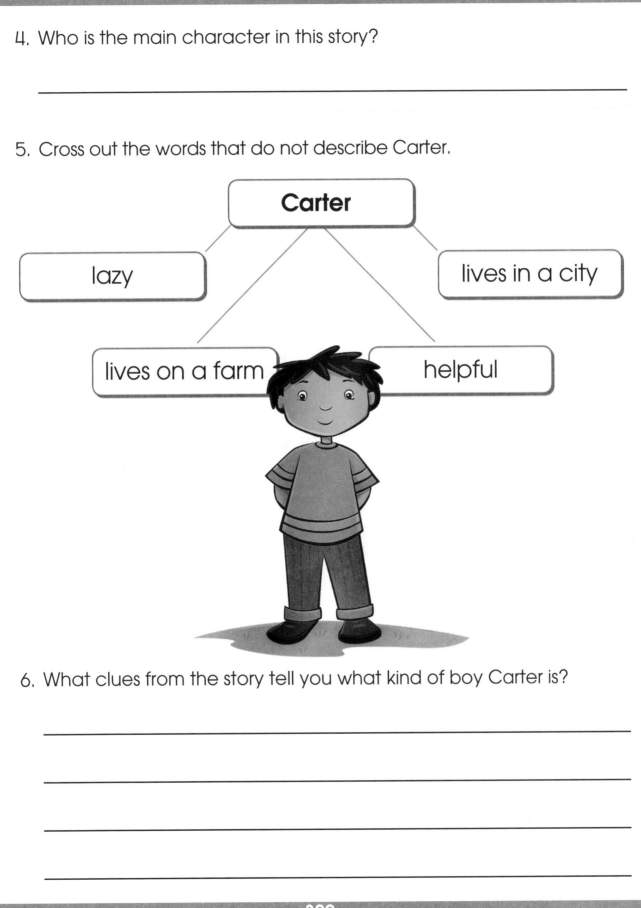

Carter

lazy

lives in a city

lives on a farm

helpful

6. What clues from the story tell you what kind of boy Carter is?

_____

_____

_____

_____

Details/Inference/Character and Setting

Read the stories. Answer the questions.

Lisa was ready for school.
She stood by the window watching for the school bus.
It stopped at the farm down the road to pick up her friends.
She would be next.

1. Where does the story takes place?

   in the city   in the woods

   by a river   in the country

Harry went to see the animals.
There were animals that came from far away places.
He knew he would not see these animals where he lived.

2. Where did Harry see the animals?

   zoo   farm

   city   school

Inference/Character and Setting

Zack's grandfather gave him a fishing rod to use.
Zack liked to fish from the dock.
Some days, ducks floated past.

3. Where did Zack fish?

    by the ocean   in the woods

    by a river   in town

Jill did not want to be late.
She must hurry before the bell rings.
She looked down the hall and saw only one door still open.

4. Where does this story take place?

    at home   at school

    at the zoo   at the store

Inference/Character and Setting

WHAT'S THE BIG IDEA?

A story is made up of a main idea and details. The **main idea** is what the story is all about. The **details** tell the things that happen in the story.

Read the story.

Ian looked out the window.
It was snowing.
He couldn't wait to get outside and play.
There were so many things he wanted to do.
First, he grabbed his sled and zoomed down the hill.
Next, he made a snowman.
After that, he built a snow fort.
Finally, Ian went inside and drank hot chocolate to warm up.
What a great day!

Answer the questions.

1. What is the story about? Circle it.

   a snowman

   Ian going sledding

   what Ian did in the snow

2. List one thing Ian did in the story.

   _____

3. List a second detail from the story.

   _____

Main Idea/Details

4. Which detail would make sense to put in the story? Circle it.

   Ian put on his roller skates.

   Ian threw snowballs at a tree.

   Ian ate ice cream to warm up.

5. Which detail does not make sense to include in the story? Circle it.

   Ian made a snow angel.

   Ian caught some snowflakes in his hand.

   Ian grabbed his swimsuit before he went outside.

6. What is the best title for this story? Circle it.

   How to Build a Snowman

   Fun in the Snow

   I Love Hot Chocolate

7. Write your own title for this story.

   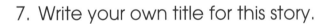

8. Draw a picture of one detail from the story.

Main Idea/Details

The **main idea** is what the entire paragraph is about.
The **details** give more information about the main idea.

Read about our solar system.

Our solar system has eight official planets. In order from the sun, they are Mercury, Venus, Earth, Mars, Jupiter, Saturn, Uranus, and Neptune. Venus is the hottest planet. Earth is the only planet with water and life. Mars may have had water at one time. Jupiter is the largest planet, and Mercury is the smallest planet. Scientists are still discovering new information about our solar system and the planets.

1. Write the main idea of the paragraph in the middle of the web.

2. Write four details from the paragraph in the web.

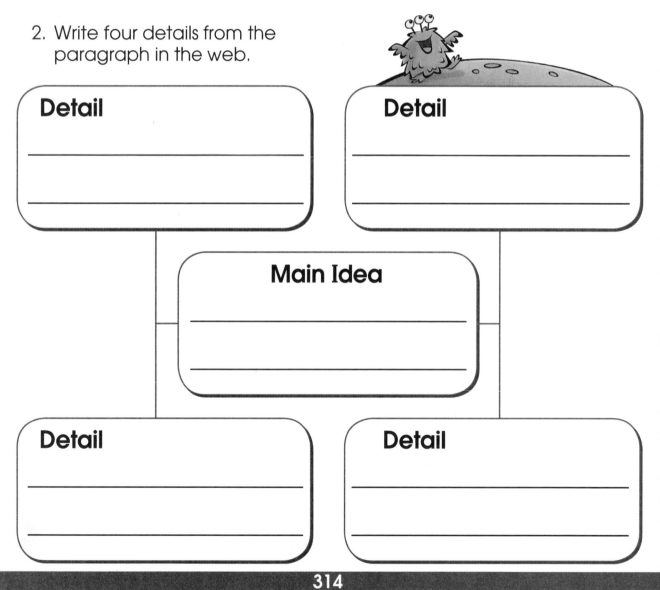

Detail

_____

_____

Detail

_____

_____

Main Idea

_____

_____

Detail

_____

_____

Detail

_____

_____

3. How many planets are in our solar system?

_____

4. List the planets in alphabetical order.

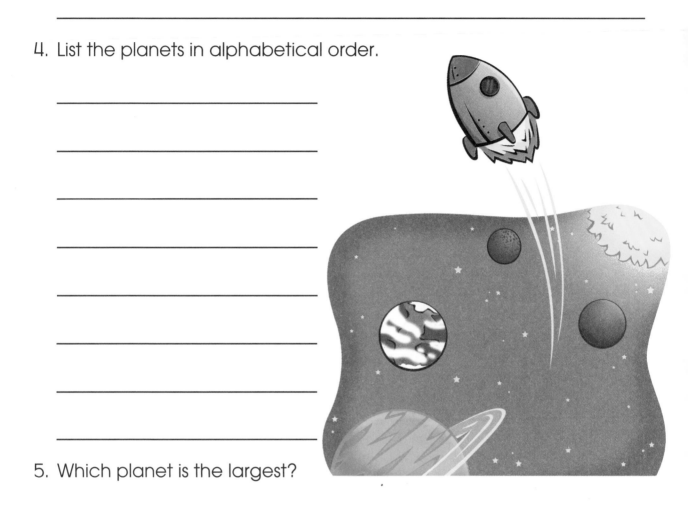

_____

_____

_____

_____

_____

_____

_____

_____

5. Which planet is the largest?

_____

6. Can humans live on any other planets? Why or why not?

_____

Write one question you have about the solar system.

_____

Main Idea/Details

Good readers do certain things while they read to help them better understand what they are reading. Use the tips below to help you while you read.

Read about the Willis Tower.

The Willis Tower, once named the Sears Tower, is the world's fifth tallest building. It was built from 1970 to 1973 in Chicago, Illinois. It has 110 stories and is 1,450 ft. high.

Tall buildings are called "skyscrapers". The Willis Tower was the tallest building in the world from 1973 to 1998. Now, the tallest structure in the world is in Dubai. The Willis Tower is still the tallest building in the United States.

1. **Set a Purpose:** Why do you want to read this?

   for fun   to learn information

2. **See It in Your Head:** Draw what you saw in your mind as you read.

3. **Ask Questions:** What questions did you have as you read?

_____

_____

4. **Predict:** Why do you think tall buildings are called "skyscrapers"?

_____

_____

5. **Evaluate:** What do you think about skyscrapers?

_____

_____

6. **Retell and Summarize:** Tell an adult what you just read. Give the main idea and details.

7. **Connect It to Your Life:** What's the tallest building you've seen?

_____

_____

_____

Reading Strategies

Read about spiders and insects.

What do you know about spiders and insects? Spiders have two body parts and eight legs. Insects have three body parts and six legs. Spiders have simple eyes and fangs. Insects have compound eyes and jaws that chew. Both spiders and insects shed their skin, which is called molting. Both are thought of as pests by people. Even though they have some things in common, spiders are not insects.

Compare and contrast spiders and insects.

Spiders
(Write some facts about spiders.)

Both
(What do they have in common?)

Insects
(Write some facts about insects.)

THE SEASONS

Read the story.

Summer is my favorite time of the year.

I can go to the beach. I can play games in my yard.

I can wear shorts and t-shirts. I can wear flip-flops.

Winter is cold. I must wear a heavy coat, a hat, and mittens.

I often have to wear boots because it has snowed.

Many winter days are without sunshine.

But, I can still play with my friends whether it's summer or winter.

coat   shorts   friends   hat   boots   t-shirts   flip-flops   beach

Write the words from the list where they belong in the diagram.

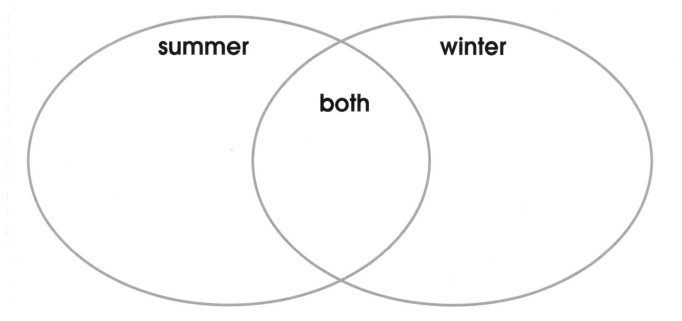

summer   winter

both

Compare and Contrast/Analysis

Read the story.

Our family has two dogs.
They are very different.
Felix likes to run after squirrels.
He barks at other dogs when he sees them.
He likes to ride in the car with us.
Benzie is our other dog.
He is getting old.
He is now very quiet and lazy.
Benzie is happy to stay at home.
Felix and Benzie have one thing they both like:
Their dinner!

lazy noisy runs young quiet old dinner

Write the words from the list where they belong in the diagram.

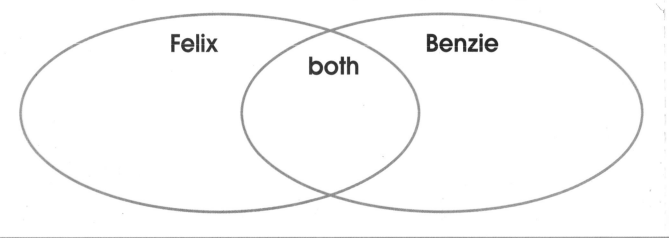

Felix   **both**   **Benzie**

Flash Action Super Reading Made Easy Workbook **08284**